BRIDLED WITH RAINBOWS

BRIDLED
WITH
RAINBOWS

Poems About Many Things Of Earth And Sky

Selected By

SARA and JOHN E. BREWTON

Decorations By

VERA BOCK

THE MACMILLAN COMPANY · NEW YORK

Copyright, 1949, by THE MACMILLAN COMPANY

All rights reserved. No part of this book may be reproduced or utilized in any form or by any means, electronic or mechanical, including photocopying, recording or by any information storage and retrieval system, without permission in writing from the Publisher.

Thirteenth Printing, 1966

PRINTED IN THE UNITED STATES OF AMERICA

ACKNOWLEDGMENTS

For permission to reprint the poems included in BRIDLED WITH RAINBOWS appreciation is expressed to the following publishers and authors:—

Appleton-Century-Crofts, Inc., New York, for "Courtesy," from *When Life Is Young* by Mary Mapes Dodge (Copyright, 1894, by the Century Company, reprinted by permission of Appleton-Century-Crofts, Inc.).

Child Life, Inc., Boston, and the authors for "Thanksgiving Magic," by Rowena Bennett (Copyright, 1944, by Child Life, Inc.); "Our History," by Catherine Cate Coblentz (Copyright, 1945, by Child Life, Inc.); "I'll Wear a Shamrock," by Mary Carolyn Davies (Copyright, 1926, by Mary Carolyn Davies); "Magic Lariat," by Glenn Ward Dresbach (Copyright, 1942, by Child Life, Inc.); "A Little Pig Asleep," by Leroy F. Jackson (Copyright, 1932, by Child Life, Inc.); "Rain Clouds," by Elizabeth-Ellen Long (Copyright, 1945, by Child Life, Inc.); "At Mrs. Appleby's," by Elizabeth Upham McWebb (Copyright, 1945, by Child Life, Inc.); "I Like House Cleaning," "Our House," and "This Is Halloween," by Dorothy Brown Thompson (Copyright, 1941, 1939, 1941, by Child Life, Inc.); "The Mist and All," by Dixie Willson (Copyright, 1924, by Child Life, Inc.); and Mrs. Arthur Guiterman for "The Christmas Exchange," by Arthur Guiterman (Copyright, 1941, by Child Life, Inc.); and Cloyd Head for "Thaw," by Eunice Tietjens (Copyright, 1939, by Child Life, Inc.); and Jessie B. Rittenhouse, Literary Executor of Clinton Scollard, for "The Quest," and "Sea Shells" (Copyright, 1926, 1925, by Child Life, Inc.).

W. Collins Sons & Company, Ltd., London, for "Who's In" from *Gammon and Spinach* by Elizabeth Fleming.

The Commonweal, New York, for "Godmother," by Phyllis B. Morden (Copyright, 1931, by *The Commonweal*).

Dodd, Mead & Company, Inc., New York, for "A Caravan from China Comes," from *New Poems* by Richard Le Gallienne; "Cradle Song," from *The Sceptred Flute* by Sarojini Naidu (Copyright, 1917, 1928, by Dodd, Mead & Company, Inc.); and for "Legacy" from *Star in a Well* by Nancy Byrd Turner (Copyright, 1935, by Dodd, Mead & Company, Inc.).

Doubleday & Company, Inc., New York, for "Good Green Bus," "If Once You Have Slept on an Island," and "Pushcart Row," from *Taxis and Toadstools* by Rachel Field (Copyright, 1926, by Doubleday & Company, Inc.); "The Boat" and "The Barge," from *Gay Go Up* by Rose Fyleman (Copyright, 1929, by Doubleday & Company, Inc.); "Best," from *The Fairy Flute* by Rose Fyleman (Copyright, 1923, by Doubleday & Company, Inc.); "Mrs. Barks," from *Fairies and Friends* by Rose Fyleman (Copyright, 1926, by Doubleday & Company, Inc.); "The Spring," from *The Fairy Green* by Rose Fyleman (Copyright, 1923, by Doubleday & Company, Inc.); "Country Trucks," "The Four-Leaf Clover," and "Raking Walnuts in the Rain," from *Goose Grass Rhymes* by Monica Shannon (Copyright, 1930, by Doubleday & Company, Inc.).

Faber & Faber, Ltd., London, and Walter de la Mare for rights of distribution in British Empire (exclusive of Canada), for "The Cupboard," "The Little Bird," "The Buckle," "The Lost Shoe," "Silver," "Somewhere," and lines from *A Child's Day*.

Harcourt, Brace and Company, Inc., New York, for "Sea-Wash," from *Smoke and Steel* by Carl Sandburg (Copyright, 1920, by Harcourt, Brace and Company, Inc.); "The Little Carved Bowl," from *Ballads and Lyrics* by Margaret Widdemer (Copyright, 1925, by Harcourt, Brace and Company, Inc.); and "The Willow Cats," from *Little Girl and Boy Land* by Margaret Widdemer (Copyright, 1924, by Harcourt, Brace and Company, Inc.).

Harper & Brothers, New York, for "Old Log House" and "Sleet Storm," from *A World to Know* by James S. Tippett (Copyright, 1933, by Harper & Brothers); "Freight Boats," from *I Go A'Traveling* by James S. Tippett (Copyright, 1929, by Harper & Brothers); "The Park," from *I Live in a City* by James S. Tippett (Copyright, 1927, by Harper & Brothers); "The Mitten Song" and "My Zipper Suit," from *A Pocketful of Rhymes* by Marie Louise Allen (Copyright, 1939, by Harper & Brothers); "Christmas in the Woods," from *Christmas in the Woods* by Frances Frost (Copyright, 1942, by Frances Frost); "Being Sick" and "The Organ Grinder," from *Puddin' an' Pie* by Jimmy Garthwaite (Copyright, 1929, by Harper & Brothers); "Night Watchmen," from *Bread an' Jam* by Wymond Garthwaite (Copyright, 1928, by Harper & Brothers).

George D. Harrap & Company, Ltd., London, for "The Grocer and the Gold-Fish," "The Harvest Elves," "Of a Spider," "The Old Inn-Sign," and "Roger Francis," from *The Happy Colt* by Wilfrid Thorley.

D. C. Heath and Company, Boston, for "Inquisitive Barn" and "Trains at Night," by Frances Frost, published in *The Packet* (Copyright, 1946, by D. C. Heath and Company).

William Heinemann, Ltd., London, for world rights other than United States of America, for "Cradle Song," from *The Sceptred Flute* by Sarojini Naidu.

Henry Holt and Company, Inc., New York, for "The Buckle," "The Cupboard," "The Little Bird," "The Lost Shoe," and "Silver," from *Collected Poems* by Walter de la Mare (Copyright, 1920, by Henry Holt and Company); "Who Pilots Ships," from *Bright Harbor* by Daniel Whitehead Hicky (Copyright, 1932, by Daniel Whitehead Hicky); four lines from *A Child's Day* by Walter de la Mare (Copyright, 1923, by Henry Holt and Company, Inc.); "Lost," from *Chicago Poems* by Carl Sandburg (Copyright, 1916, by Henry Holt and Company, Inc.).

Houghton Mifflin Company, Boston, for "The Cloud," from *A Pocketful of Posies* by Abbie Farwell Brown (Copyright, 1902, by Abbie Farwell Brown); and "Fringed Gentians" and "The Sea Shell," from *A Dome of Many Coloured Glass* by Amy Lowell (Copyright, 1912, by Amy Lowell). Each of these selections is used by permission of, and by arrangement with, Houghton Mifflin Company.

Alfred A. Knopf, Inc., New York, for "Seascape," from *The Dream Keeper* by Langston Hughes (Copyright, 1932, by Alfred A. Knopf, Inc.).

J. B. Lippincott Company, Philadelphia, for "City Streets and Country Roads," from *Joan's Door* by Eleanor Farjeon (Copyright, 1926, by J. B. Lippincott Company); "Geography," "School-Bell," and "Who'll Buy My Valley Lilies?" from *Sing for Your Supper* by Eleanor Farjeon (Copyright, 1938, by Eleanor Farjeon); "Moonbeam," from *Shoes of the Wind* by Hilda Conkling (Copyright, 1922, by J. B. Lippincott Company).

Little, Brown & Company, Boston, for "I'll Tell You How the Sun Rose," from *The Poems of Emily Dickinson* edited by Martha Dickinson Bianchi and Alfred Leete Hampson (Copyright, 1890, 1891, 1896, by Roberts Brothers; copyright, 1914, 1918, 1919, 1924, 1929, 1930, by Martha Dickinson Bianchi); and "The Mermaidens," from *Tirra Lirra* by Laura E. Richards (Copyright, 1918, 1930, 1932, by Laura E. Richards).

Lothrop, Lee & Shepard Co., Inc., New York, for "Nutting Time," from *Rhyme Time for Children* by Emilie Poulsson (Copyright, 1929, by Lothrop, Lee & Shepard Co., Inc.).

Robert M. McBride & Company, New York, for "Bells in the Country," from *Youth Grows Old* by Robert Nathan (Copyright, 1922, by Robert M. McBride & Company).

David McKay Company, Philadelphia, for "Being a Gypsy" and "Road Fellows," from *Christopher O!* by Barbara Young (Copyright, 1947, by Barbara Young).

Rand McNally & Company, Chicago, for "All Aboard for Bombay" and "I've Got a New

Book from My Grandfather Hyde," from *The Peter Patter Book* by Leroy F. Jackson (Copyright, 1918, renewal copyright, 1946, by Rand McNally & Company, Publishers).

The Macmillan Company, New York, for "Eggs," "The Frowning Cliff," "Skating," and "A Ship Sails up to Bideford," from *Pillicock Hill* by Herbert Asquith; "Turtle Soup," from *Collected Verse* by Lewis Carroll; "The Falling Star," "Full Moon: Santa Barbara," and "Night," from *Stars Tonight* by Sara Teasdale (Copyright, 1930, by Sara Teasdale Filsinger); "A Swing Song," from *Robin Redbreast and Other Verses* by William Allingham; "Christmas," "Easter Parade," "Food," and "My Plan" from *Rhymes About the City* by Marchette Chute (Copyright, 1946, by The Macmillan Company); "Presents," from *Rhymes About Ourselves* by Marchette Chute (Copyright, 1932, by The Macmillan Company); "The Axe Has Cut the Forest Down" and "This Is the Hay That No Man Planted," from *Away Goes Sally* by Elizabeth Coatsworth (Copyright, 1934, by The Macmillan Company); "Sometimes a Little House Will Please," "This Air That Blows in from the Sea," and "What Could Be Lovelier Than to Hear," from *The Littlest House* by Elizabeth Coatsworth (Copyright, 1940, by The Macmillan Company); "The Storm Snapped Its Fingers," from *The Fair American* by Elizabeth Coatsworth (Copyright, 1940, by The Macmillan Company); "Almost" and "Roads," from *The Pointed People* by Rachel Field (Copyright, 1924 and 1930, by The Macmillan Company); "Something Told the Wild Geese," from *Branches Green* by Rachel Field (Copyright, 1934, by The Macmillan Company); "The Dandelion" and "The Moon's the North Wind's Cooky," from *Johnny Appleseed and Other Poems* by Vachel Lindsay (Copyright, 1913, 1914, 1917, 1925, and 1928, by The Macmillan Company); "Boats Sail on the Rivers," "But Give Me Holly, Bold and Jolly," "Clouds," "Growing in the Vale," "My Gift," "O Sailor, Come Ashore," "Who Has Seen the Wind?" and "The Wind Has Such a Rainy Sound," from *Sing-Song* by Christina G. Rossetti; "Autumn Fires," "Escape at Bedtime," and "Happy Thought," from *A Child's Garden of Verses* by Robert Louis Stevenson.

Oxford University Press, London, for "White Horses," from *Out of the Everywhere* by Winifred Howard.

Poetry, Chicago, for "Mockery," by Katherine Dixon Riggs, and "Who Loves the Rain," by Frances Shaw (Copyright, 1920, 1914, by *Poetry Magazine*).

Rinehart & Company, Inc., New York, for "Bible Stories," from *The Selected Poems of Lizette Woodworth Reese* (Copyright, 1926, by Lizette Woodworth Reese); and "A Little Song of Life," from *A Wayside Lute* by Lizette Woodworth Reese (Copyright, 1909, by Thomas B. Mosher).

Sidgwick & Jackson, Ltd., London, for "Choosing Shoes," from *The Very Thing* by ffrida Wolfe.

The Society of Authors, London, as the Literary Representative of the Estate of the late Richard Le Gallienne, for world rights excluding the United States, for "A Caravan from China Comes," from *New Poems*; and to Rose Fyleman, The Society of Authors, and Methuen & Co., Ltd., London, for world rights excluding the United States, for "The Barge," "Best," "The Boats," "Mrs. Barks," and "The Spring."

Story Parade, Inc., New York, for "A Modern Ballad (The Ups and Downs of the Elevator Car)," by Caroline D. Emerson (Copyright, 1936, by Story Parade, Inc.); "Proud Hollyhock," by Marguerite Buller (Copyright, 1936, by Story Parade, Inc.); "Hump, the Escalator," by Dorothy Faubion (Copyright, 1942, by Story Parade, Inc.); "Winds A-Blowing," by May Justus (Copyright, 1940, by Story Parade, Inc.); "Kite Days," by Mark Sawyer (Copyright, 1939, by Story Parade, Inc.); "The Wind," by Betty Miller (Copyright, 1937, by Story Parade, Inc.); and "The Pear Tree," by E. Elizabeth Longwell (Copyright, 1943, by Story Parade, Inc.).

The Viking Press, Inc., New York, for "Somewhere," from *Bells and Grass* by Walter de la Mare (Copyright, 1942, by Walter de la Mare); "Words from an Old Spanish Carol," from *The Long Christmas* by Ruth Sawyer (Copyright, 1941, by Ruth Sawyer); "Autumn Fields," from *Under the Tree* by Elizabeth Madox Roberts (Copyright, 1922, by B. W.

Huebsch, Inc.). Each of these selections is used by permission of The Viking Press, Inc., New York.

Ann Watkins, Inc., and the author of "Farm Cart" and "Sailor," from *Cherrystones* by Eleanor Farjeon (Copyright, 1942, by Eleanor Farjeon); for world rights excluding the United States and Canada for "Geography," "School-Bell," and "Who'll Buy My Valley Lilies?" from *Sing for Your Supper* by Eleanor Farjeon (Copyright, 1938, by Eleanor Farjeon); and for world rights excluding the United States and Canada for "City Streets and Country Roads," from *Joan's Door* by Eleanor Farjeon (Copyright, 1926, by J. B. Lippincott Company).

The John C. Winston Company, Philadelphia, for "An Indignant Male," from *Five Going on Six* by A. B. Ross (Copyright, 1927, by The John C. Winston Company).

Yale University Press, New Haven, Conn., for "Bundles," "Choice," "A Comparison," and "The Drum," from *Songs for Parents* by John Farrar (Copyright, 1921, by Yale University Press).

George E. Abbot for "Why Does It Snow" from *Merry-Go-Round* by Laura E. Richards (Copyright, 1935, by D. Appleton-Century Company).

Cynthia Asquith, Literary Executor of Herbert Asquith for world rights excluding the United States for "Eggs," "The Frowning Cliff," "Skating," and "A Ship Sails up to Bideford," from *Pillicock Hill* by Herbert Asquith.

Peggy Bacon for "Darkness," published in *Story Parade* (Copyright, 1936, by Peggy Bacon).

Dorothy W. Baruch for "Merry-Go-Round" and "The Popcorn-Popper," from *I Like Machinery*, published by Harper & Brothers (Copyright, 1933, by Harper & Brothers).

H. H. Bashford for "Parliament Hill," from *Songs Out of School*.

K. M. Brewer for lines from *Songs of Manhattan* by Morris Abel Beer (Copyright, 1918, by The Cornhill Company).

Mary Jane Carr for "The Big Swing-Tree Is Green Again," "The Castle in the Fire," "Pirate Wind," "Shop of Dreams," "The West Wind's Secret," and "When a Ring's Around the Moon," from *Top of the Morning* (Copyright, 1941, by Mary Jane Carr).

Joseph S. Cotter, Sr., for "Rain Music," from *The Band of Gideon* by Joseph S. Cotter, Jr. (Copyright, 1918, by The Cornhill Company).

Nona Keen Duffy and *American Junior Red Cross News* for "Above the Stable" (Copyright, 1945, by *American Junior Red Cross News*).

Ivy O. Eastwick and *Jack and Jill* for "May Mornings" (Copyright, 1947, by *Jack and Jill*); and two lines from "The Fairy Land Express" (Copyright, 1946, by *Jack and Jill*).

John Farrar for "Threnody," from *Songs for Johnny-Jump-Up* (Copyright, 1930, by Richard R. Smith, Inc.).

Frances Frost and *American Junior Red Cross News* for "Apple Season," "Easter in the Woods," "Rambunctious Brook," and "Sniff" (Copyright, 1942, 1945, 1944, by *American Junior Red Cross News*).

Mrs. Arthur Guiterman for "Indian Pipe and Moccasin Flower," by Arthur Guiterman from *The Light Guitar* published by Harper & Brothers (Copyright, 1923, by Harper & Brothers).

Carolyn Haywood and *Jack and Jill* for "Little Clown Puppet" (Copyright, 1938, by *Jack and Jill*).

Cloyd Head and *Story Parade* for "Old Maps," by Eunice Tietjens (Copyright, 1936, by Eunice Tietjens).

Daniel Whitehead Hicky for "The Runaway," published in *Good Housekeeping* (Copyright, 1936, by Daniel Whitehead Hicky).

Valine Hobbs and *The Horn Book Magazine* for "One Day When We Went Walking" (Copyright, 1947, by The Horn Book, Inc.).

Dr. Francis A. Litz for "High and Low," from *The Poetry of Father Tabb*, by John Banister Tabb (Copyright, 1902, 1923, 1928, by Francis A. Litz).

Mary Ellen Lynde and *The New York Times* for "Queen Anne's Lace" by Mary Leslie Newton (Copyright, 1923, by *The New York Times*).

David McCord and *The Saturday Review of Literature* for "The Frost Pane" (Copyright, 1926, by *The Saturday Review of Literature*).

Mary Maxtone for "Skywriting," published in *Good Housekeeping* (Copyright, 1947, by Janet Maxtone-Graham).

Luella Markley Mockett and *Jack and Jill* for "The Haymow" (Copyright, 1940, by *Jack and Jill*).

J. Paget-Fredericks for "Pipings," from Green-Pipes (Copyright, 1929, by The Macmillan Company).

Nell Goodale Price and *Jack and Jill* for "School Begins" (Copyright, 1942, by *Jack and Jill*).

Dorothy Brown Thompson for "The City and the Trucks" and "Maps" (Copyright, 1935, by Dorothy Brown Thompson).

Nancy Byrd Turner for "A Word About Woodpiles."

Hilda Van Stockum and *The Horn Book Magazine* for "The Hut" (Copyright, 1943, by The Horn Book, Inc.).

Susan Adger Williams for "Pockets," published in *Good Housekeeping* (Copyright, 1930, by Susan Adger Williams).

Kathryn Worth for "Circus Elephant" and "Smells," from *Poems for Josephine*, published by Doubleday and Company, Inc. (Copyright, 1943, by Kathyrn Worth Curry).

TO

George Meredith Blackburn, Jr.

Little White Horses are out on the sea,
  Bridled with rainbows and speckled with foam,
Laden with presents for you and for me,
  Mermaids and fairies are riding them home!

—Winifred Howard

FOREWORD

Eleven years ago, in *Under the Tent of the Sky*, we shared with you poems about animals large and small which we thought delightful. Three years later, in *Gaily We Parade*, we shared with you poems about a gay procession of people—all kinds—home folk, town folk, country folk, funny folk, fairy folk, royal folk, even folk that never were except in fancy.

In *Bridled with Rainbows*, we give you more poems of pure delight—poems about the many things of earth and sky. Of these things Robert Louis Stevenson was thinking when he said:

> The world is so full of a number of things,
> I'm sure we should all be as happy as kings.

And Sara Teasdale when she wrote:

> Life has loveliness to sell,
> All beautiful and splendid things . . .

And Rachel Field when she said:

> There are things you almost see
> In the woods of evening—
> Fairies as thick as fireflies,
> Elves leaping in a ring.
>
> There are things you almost hear
> When no one passes by—
> Stirring of seeds in good damp earth,
> Stars marching through the sky.

So, in *Bridled with Rainbows*, we give you these beautiful splendid things of earth and sky. And remember "the safe-kept memory of a lovely thing" is "better than the minting of a gold-crowned king."

September, 1948

Sara Westbrook Brewton
John Edmund Brewton

CONTENTS

OFF TO SOMEWHERE

Roads	RACHEL FIELD	3
The Old Inn-Sign	WILFRID THORLEY	4
Road Fellows	BARBARA YOUNG	5
Maps	DOROTHY BROWN THOMPSON	6
Trains at Night	FRANCES FROST	7
The Railroad Cars Are Coming	AUTHOR UNKNOWN	7
The Edge of the World	MARY FANNY YOUNGS	8
All Aboard for Bombay	LEROY F. JACKSON	8
Sailor	ELEANOR FARJEON	9
The Barge	ROSE FYLEMAN	10
The Boat	ROSE FYLEMAN	10
If Once You Have Slept on an Island	RACHEL FIELD	11
Being a Gypsy	BARBARA YOUNG	12
Somewhere	WALTER DE LA MARE	13

WHAT WE WEAR—O DEARIE ME

Best	ROSE FYLEMAN	17
Elizabeth Ann Peabody	IVY O. EASTWICK	18
The Mitten Song	MARIE LOUISE ALLEN	19
An Indignant Male	A. B. ROSS	20
My Zipper Suit	MARIE LOUISE ALLEN	20
Bryan O'Lin Had No Breeches to Wear	MOTHER GOOSE	21
The Bonnie Cravat	MOTHER GOOSE	21
Bobby Shaftoe's Gone to Sea	MOTHER GOOSE	21
The Lost Shoe	WALTER DE LA MARE	22
Choosing Shoes	FFRIDA WOLFE	23
Galoshes	RHODA W. BACMEISTER	24
High and Low	JOHN BANISTER TABB	24
Courtesy	MARY MAPES DODGE	25
The Buckle	WALTER DE LA MARE	25
Pockets	SUSAN ADGER WILLIAMS	26

COME, LET US PLAY

One Day When We Went Walking	VALINE HOBBS	29
The Pear Tree	E. ELIZABETH LONGWELL	30
Girls and Boys, Come Out to Play	MOTHER GOOSE	31
Little Clown Puppet	CAROLYN HAYWOOD	32
Skating	HERBERT ASQUITH	33
Merry-Go-Round	DOROTHY WALTER BARUCH	34
My Plan	MARCHETTE CHUTE	35
The Big Swing-Tree Is Green Again	MARY JANE CARR	35
A Swing Song	WILLIAM ALLINGHAM	36
The Hut	HILDA VAN STOCKUM	37
The Drum	JOHN FARRAR	38
The Haymow	LUELLA MARKLEY MOCKETT	39
Pipings	J. PAGET-FREDERICKS	40

GO DANCING TO SCHOOL

May Mornings	IVY O. EASTWICK	43
School-Bell	ELEANOR FARJEON	43
School Begins	NELL GOODALE PRICE	44
Being Sick	JIMMY GARTHWAITE	44
I've Got a New Book from My Grandfather Hyde	LEROY F. JACKSON	44
Roger Francis	WILFRID THORLEY	45
Our History	CATHERINE CATE COBLENTZ	46
Multiplication Is Vexation	MOTHER GOOSE	46
Geography	ELEANOR FARJEON	46
Old Maps	EUNICE TIETJENS	47
The Organ-Grinder	JIMMY GARTHWAITE	48
Sniff	FRANCES FROST	48

BELLS IN THE COUNTRY

Bells in the Country	ROBERT NATHAN	51
City Streets and Country Roads	ELEANOR FARJEON	52
Country Trucks	MONICA SHANNON	52

xiv

Mad Farmer's Song	AUTHOR UNKNOWN	53
Legacy	NANCY BYRD TURNER	54
The Axe Has Cut the Forest Down	ELIZABETH COATSWORTH	55
Eggs	HERBERT ASQUITH	55
Inquisitive Barn	FRANCES FROST	56
A Little Pig Asleep	LEROY F. JACKSON	56
Farm Cart	ELEANOR FARJEON	57
Jack Sprat's Pig	MOTHER GOOSE	57
Raking Walnuts in the Rain	MONICA SHANNON	58
The Quest	CLINTON SCOLLARD	58
Blow, Wind, Blow! And Go, Mill, Go	MOTHER GOOSE	59
Autumn Fields	ELIZABETH MADOX ROBERTS	59
The Harvest Elves	WILFRID THORLEY	60
The Runaway	DANIEL WHITEHEAD HICKY	61
The Dandelion	VACHEL LINDSAY	62
Growing in the Vale	CHRISTINA G. ROSSETTI	62
The Four-Leaf Clover	MONICA SHANNON	63
Queen Anne's Lace	MARY LESLIE NEWTON	63
Fringed Gentians	AMY LOWELL	64
A Comparison	JOHN FARRAR	65
The Willow Cats	MARGARET WIDDEMER	65
A Little Song of Life	LIZETTE WOODWORTH REESE	66

THIS IS THE WONDROUS CITY

Good Green Bus	RACHEL FIELD	69
Mrs. Barks	ROSE FYLEMAN	70
Pushcart Row	RACHEL FIELD	71
Who'll Buy My Valley Lilies?	ELEANOR FARJEON	72
Food	MARCHETTE CHUTE	72
The Grocer and the Gold-Fish	WILFRID THORLEY	73
The Popcorn-Popper	DOROTHY WALTER BARUCH	74
The City and the Trucks	DOROTHY BROWN THOMPSON	75
A Modern Ballad (The Ups and Downs of the Elevator Car)	CAROLINE D. EMERSON	76
Hump, The Escalator	DOROTHY FAUBION	77

It Is Raining	LUCY SPRAGUE MITCHELL	78
The Park	JAMES S. TIPPETT	78
Daffy-Down-Dilly	MOTHER GOOSE	78
The Bells of London	AUTHOR UNKNOWN	79
Parliament Hill	H. H. BASHFORD	80

WHERE THE RED FOX HIDES

Dark Danny	IVY O. EASTWICK	83
Circus Elephant	KATHRYN WORTH	84
The Spring	ROSE FYLEMAN	85
Rambunctious Brook	FRANCES FROST	85
Mickleham Way	IVY O. EASTWICK	86
Indian Pipe and Moccasin Flower	ARTHUR GUITERMAN	88
Laughing Song	WILLIAM BLAKE	88
The West Wind's Secret	MARY JANE CARR	89
Midsummer Magic	IVY O. EASTWICK	90
Blessed of the Lord Be His Land	THE BIBLE	92
Pippa's Song	ROBERT BROWNING	92

DEEP IN THE SKY

When a Ring's Around the Moon	MARY JANE CARR	95
Mockery	KATHERINE DIXON RIGGS	96
Moonbeam	HILDA CONKLING	97
The Moon's the North Wind's Cooky	VACHEL LINDSAY	97
Silver	WALTER DE LA MARE	98
Full Moon: Santa Barbara	SARA TEASDALE	98
Night	SARA TEASDALE	99
Stars	RHODA W. BACMEISTER	99
The Falling Star	SARA TEASDALE	99
A Caravan from China Comes	RICHARD LE GALLIENNE	100
Escape at Bedtime	ROBERT LOUIS STEVENSON	101
Darkness	PEGGY BACON	101
Clouds	CHRISTINA G. ROSSETTI	102
Boats Sail on the Rivers	CHRISTINA G. ROSSETTI	102
I'll Tell You How the Sun Rose	EMILY DICKINSON	103
Skywriting	MARY MAXTONE	104

HAPPY BE THE WEATHER

Something Told the Wild Geese	RACHEL FIELD	107
Winds A-Blowing	MAY JUSTUS	108
Who Has Seen the Wind?	CHRISTINA G. ROSSETTI	108
The Wind	BETTY MILLER	109
Who Loves the Rain	FRANCES SHAW	110
Apple Season	FRANCES FROST	110
Pirate Wind	MARY JANE CARR	111
Autumn Fires	ROBERT LOUIS STEVENSON	112
Nutting Time	EMILIE POULSSON	112
The Mist and All	DIXIE WILLSON	113
October's Party	GEORGE COOPER	114
Threnody	JOHN FARRAR	115
Why Does It Snow?	LAURA E. RICHARDS	116
The Frost Pane	DAVID MCCORD	117
A Devonshire Rhyme	AUTHOR UNKNOWN	118
Sleet Storm	JAMES S. TIPPETT	118
Thaw	EUNICE TIETJENS	119
Kite Days	MARK SAWYER	119
Smells	KATHRYN WORTH	120
Rain Clouds	ELIZABETH-ELLEN LONG	121
Rain Music	JOSEPH S. COTTER, JR.	122
What Could Be Lovelier Than to Hear	ELIZABETH COATSWORTH	123
The Song on the Way	AUTHOR UNKNOWN	124

SHIPS AND SEAS

The Sea Shell	AMY LOWELL	127
Sea Shells	CLINTON SCOLLARD	127
The Mermaidens	LAURA E. RICHARDS	128
O Sailor, Come Ashore	CHRISTINA G. ROSSETTI	128
This Is the Hay That No Man Planted	ELIZABETH COATSWORTH	129
This Air That Blows in from the Sea	ELIZABETH COATSWORTH	130

The Frowning Cliff	HERBERT ASQUITH	131
Sea-Wash	CARL SANDBURG	131
A Ship Sails up to Bideford	HERBERT ASQUITH	132
The Wind Has Such a Rainy Sound	CHRISTINA G. ROSSETTI	133
Seascape	LANGSTON HUGHES	133
Lost	CARL SANDBURG	134
Freight Boats	JAMES S. TIPPETT	135
The Storm Snapped Its Fingers	ELIZABETH COATSWORTH	136
White Horses	WINIFRED HOWARD	137
Who Pilots Ships	DANIEL WHITEHEAD HICKY	138

JOLLY DAYS

The New Year	DINAH M. MULOCK CRAIK	141
I'll Wear a Shamrock	MARY CAROLYN DAVIES	141
Easter in the Woods	FRANCES FROST	142
Easter Parade	MARCHETTE CHUTE	142
Choice	JOHN FARRAR	143
This Is Halloween	DOROTHY BROWN THOMPSON	144
Thanksgiving Magic	ROWENA BASTIN BENNETT	145
Christmas Greeting	AUTHOR UNKNOWN	146
But Give Me Holly, Bold and Jolly	CHRISTINA G. ROSSETTI	146
The Christmas Exchange	ARTHUR GUITERMAN	146
Bundles	JOHN FARRAR	147
Presents	MARCHETTE CHUTE	147
Christmas	MARCHETTE CHUTE	148
My Gift	CHRISTINA G. ROSSETTI	148
Words from an Old Spanish Carol	RUTH SAWYER	149
Long, Long Ago	AUTHOR UNKNOWN	150
Above the Stable	NONA KEEN DUFFY	150
Christmas in the Woods	FRANCES FROST	151
Christmas Carol	AUTHOR UNKNOWN	152

A LITTLE HOUSE WILL PLEASE

Sometimes a Little House Will Please	ELIZABETH COATSWORTH	155
Our House	DOROTHY BROWN THOMPSON	156

The Little Bird	WALTER DE LA MARE	157
Old Log House	JAMES S. TIPPETT	158
I Like House Cleaning	DOROTHY BROWN THOMPSON	159
Cross Patch	MOTHER GOOSE	160
The Castle in the Fire	MARY JANE CARR	160
A Word About Woodpiles	NANCY BYRD TURNER	161
At Mrs. Appleby's	ELIZABETH UPHAM MCWEBB	162
Godmother	PHYLLIS B. MORDEN	163
Bible Stories	LIZETTE WOODWORTH REESE	164
The Little Carved Bowl	MARGARET WIDDEMER	165
Who's In	ELIZABETH FLEMING	166
House Blessing	ARTHUR GUITERMAN	166
A Child's Grace	ROBERT BURNS	167
When Jacky's a Very Good Boy	MOTHER GOOSE	167
Nose, Nose, Jolly Red Nose	MOTHER GOOSE	167
Polly Put the Kettle On	MOTHER GOOSE	167
The Cupboard	WALTER DE LA MARE	168
Turtle Soup	LEWIS CARROLL	169
Wash the Dishes, Wipe the Dishes	MOTHER GOOSE	169
Magic Lariat	GLENN WARD DRESBACH	170
Of a Spider	WILFRID THORLEY	170
Mistress Mary, Quite Contrary	MOTHER GOOSE	171
Proud Hollyhock	MARGUERITE BULLER	171
Night Watchmen	WYMOND GARTHWAITE	172
Deedle, Deedle, Dumpling, My Son John	MOTHER GOOSE	172
Shop of Dreams	MARY JANE CARR	173
Cradle Song	SAROJINI NAIDU	174
Good Night	DOROTHY MASON PIERCE	174

OFF TO SOMEWHERE

I want to be off to Somewhere

To far, lone, lovely Somewhere,

No matter where Somewhere be.

—Walter de la Mare

ROADS

A road might lead to anywhere—
    To harbor towns and quays,
Or to a witch's pointed house
    Hidden by bristly trees.
It might lead past the tailor's door,
    Where he sews with needle and thread,
Or by Miss Pim the milliner's,
    With her hats for every head.
It might be a road to a great, dark cave
    With treasure and gold piled high,
Or a road with a mountain tied to its end,
    Blue-humped against the sky.
Oh, a road might lead you anywhere—
    To Mexico or Maine.
But then, it might just fool you, and—
    Lead you back home again!
                      —*Rachel Field*

THE OLD INN-SIGN
(1825)

The roadway has a flinten face
   And breath is like a steam,
While loud and taut upon the trace
   Comes on the cantering team.
For at my Inn the coaches stop,
   The fares they stay to dine
When horses' hoofs come *clip-a-clop,*
   Clip-a-clop, clip-a-clop,
   Before the old Inn-sign.

Now fetch your faggots in, good lass!
   Good ostler fetch your hay!
And let the time in comfort pass
   While man and horse delay.
For cheerless is the coach's top
   And heavy is the load
When horses' hoofs go *clip-a-clop,*
   Clip-a-clop, clip-a-clop,
   Along the frosty road.

Now show the dame into her chair,
   Unboot her weary lord,
And set before them both good fare
   With flagons on the board,
For welcome is the coach's stop,
   And bravely shall they dine
When horses' hoofs come *clip-a-clop,*
   Clip-a-clop, clip-a-clop,
   Before the old Inn-sign.
          —*Wilfrid Thorley*

ROAD FELLOWS

Little Tillie Turtle
Went a-walking down the road
And happened at the corner
On little Tommy Toad.
"Good-morning, Sir," said Tillie.
"Good-morning, Ma'am," said he,
And they strolled along together
As cosy as could be.

And when they reached the orchard,
As sure as you're alive,
They saw big Billy Bumble-bee
Emerging from his hive.
"Good-morning, friends," said Billy.
"Good-morning, Sir," said they.
"We're very glad to notice
That you're going down our way."

Along they sauntered gaily,
Till on a wayside stone
They saw young Benny Beetle Bug
A-sitting there alone.
"Good-morning, Sir," they caroled.
"Good-morning all, to you,"
Said Benny, "are you traveling?
I'd like to travel, too."
They beckoned him politely;
He followed with a will.
And if they haven't stopped for tea
I think they're strolling still.
—*Barbara Young*

MAPS

High adventure
    And bright dream—
Maps are mightier
    Than they seem:

Ships that follow
    Leaning stars—
Red and gold of
    Strange bazaars—

Ice floes hid
    Beyond all knowing—
Planes that ride where
    Winds are blowing!

Train maps, maps of
    Wind and weather,
Road maps—taken
    Altogether

Maps are really
    Magic wands
For home-staying
    Vagabonds!
      —*Dorothy Brown Thompson*

TRAINS AT NIGHT

I like the whistle of trains at night,
The fast trains thundering by so proud!
They rush and rumble across the world,
They ring wild bells and they toot so loud!

But I love better the slower trains.
They take their time through the world instead,
And whistle softly and stop to tuck
Each sleepy blinking town in bed!
—*Frances Frost*

THE RAILROAD CARS ARE COMING

The great Pacific railway,
  For California hail!
Bring on the locomotive,
  Lay down the iron rail;
Across the rolling prairies
  By steam we're bound to go,
The railroad cars are coming, humming
  Through New Mexico,
The railroad cars are coming, humming
  Through New Mexico.
The little dogs in dog-town
  Will wag each little tail;
They'll think that something's coming
  A-riding on a rail.
The rattlesnake will show its fangs,
  The owl to-whit, tu-who,
The railroad cars are coming, humming
  Through New Mexico,
The railroad cars are coming, humming
  Through New Mexico.
—*Author Unknown*

THE EDGE OF THE WORLD[1]

From the top of the bluff, where the wind blows free,
Clear out to the edge of the world I see,
And I look and look, till my eyes grow dim,
But I can't see what lies over the rim!

I see the steamers go in towards town;
I watch the schooners sail slowly down—
Down out of sight, and far away—
Oh! I shall sail over the rim, some day.

Over the rim and far beyond,
To Hong-Kong and Bagdad and Trebizond,
And Ceylon's Isle, where the breezes blow,
And the Happy Harbor, where good ships go.

And it may be bad, or it may be fair,
And I may come back, or I may stay there,
But one thing is sure—be it gay or grim,
Some day—some day—I must cross that rim!

—*Mary Fanny Youngs*

ALL ABOARD FOR BOMBAY

All aboard for Bombay,
    All aboard for Rome!
Leave your little sisters
    And your loving aunts at home.

Bring a bit of bailing wire,
    A pocketful of nails,
And half a dozen wienewursts
    For every man that sails.

---

[1] Taken from *When We Were Little*, by Mary Fanny Youngs, published and copyright, 1919, renewed 1947, by E. P. Dutton & Co., Inc., New York.

Tell Terry Tagg, when you go by,
  Be sure to bring his dog.
All aboard for Bombay
  On a floating cedar log!
          —*Leroy F. Jackson*

SAILOR

My sweetheart's a Sailor,
He sails on the sea,
When he comes home
He brings presents for me;
Coral from China,
Silks from Siam,
Parrots and pearls
From Seringapatam,
Silver from Mexico,
Gold from Peru,
Indian feathers
From Kalamazoo,
Scents from Sumatra,
Mantillas from Spain,
A fisherman's float
From the waters of Maine,
Reindeers from Lapland,
Ducks from Bombay,
A unicorn's horn
From the Land of Cathay—
Isn't it lucky
For someone like me
To marry a Sailor
Who sails on the sea!
         —*Eleanor Farjeon*

THE BARGE

I saw a great barge
  On the river to-day
All roomy and large,
  All painted and gay.
And only a boy
  And a dog were in charge . . .
Oh, think what a joy
  To look after a barge.
       —*Rose Fyleman*

THE BOAT

Sleeping in a cabin is as jolly as can be,
And it's fun to throw your rubbish out straight into the sea;
And the captain is so handsome, with gold upon his coat,
And I do like living on a boat.

The steward gives me apples, and orange juice to drink,
And the lamps are lit at lunch time, all beautiful and pink;
And there's soup with little letters in, and lovely stripy ice,
And when the floor went wobbly it was nice.

We haven't seen a mermaid, we haven't had a wreck,
But I've never known a nursery so thrilling as a deck;
I never do a lesson, I never play a note . . .
I do like living on a boat.
       —*Rose Fyleman*

IF ONCE YOU HAVE SLEPT ON AN ISLAND

If once you have slept on an island
    You'll never be quite the same;
You may look as you looked the day before
    And go by the same old name,

You may bustle about in street and shop;
    You may sit at home and sew,
But you'll see blue water and wheeling gulls
    Wherever your feet may go.

You may chat with the neighbors of this and that
    And close to your fire keep,
But you'll hear ship whistle and lighthouse bell
    And tides beat through your sleep.

Oh, you won't know why, and you can't say how
    Such change upon you came,
But—once you have slept on an island
    You'll never be quite the same!

                      —*Rachel Field*

BEING A GYPSY

A gypsy, a gypsy,
Is what I'd like to be,
If ever I could find one who
Would change his place with me.

Rings on my fingers,
Earrings in my ears,
Rough shoes to roam the world
For years and years and years!

I'd listen to the stars,
I'd listen to the dawn,
I'd learn the tunes of wind and rain,
The talk of fox and faun.

A gypsy, a gypsy!
To ramble and to roam
For maybe—oh,
A week or so—
And then I'd hie me home!

—*Barbara Young*

SOMEWHERE

Would you tell me the way to Somewhere?
   Somewhere, *Some*where,
   I have heard of a place called Somewhere—
   But know not where it can be.
      It makes no difference,
      Whether or not
      I go in dreams
      Or trudge on foot:
Could you tell me the way to Somewhere,
   The Somewhere meant for me?

There's a little old house in Somewhere—
   *Some*where, *Some*where,
A queer little house, with a Cat and a Mouse—
   Just room enough for three.
      A kitchen, a larder,
      A bin for bread,
      A string of candles,
      Or stars instead,
      A table, a chair,
      And a four-post bed—
There's room for us all in Somewhere,
   For the Cat and the Mouse and Me.

Puss is called *Skimme* in Somewhere,
   In *Some*where, *Some*where;
   Miaou, miaou, in Somewhere,
   S—K—I—M—M—E.
      Miss Mouse is scarcely
      One inch tall,
      So *she* never needed
      A name at all;

> And though you call,
> And call, and call,
> There squeaks no answer,
> Great or small—
Though her tail is a sight times longer
> Than this is likely to be:—
> > FOR
I want to be *off* to Somewhere,
To far, lone, lovely Somewhere,
No matter where Somewhere be.

> It makes no difference
> Whether or not
> I flit in sleep
> Or trudge on foot,
> Or this time tomorrow
> How far I've got,
> Summer or Winter,
> Cold, or hot,
> Where, or When,
> Or Why, or What—
Please, tell me the way to Somewhere—
> *Somewhere, Somewhere;*
Somewhere, *Somewhere, Somewhere,* SOMEWHERE—
> The Somewhere meant for me!
> > *—Walter de la Mare*

WHAT WE WEAR—
O DEARIE ME

But what we wear—O dearie me!—
Is naught but a patch upon what we be.
And rags and tatters often hide
A brave little body bunched up inside.
—*Walter de la Mare*

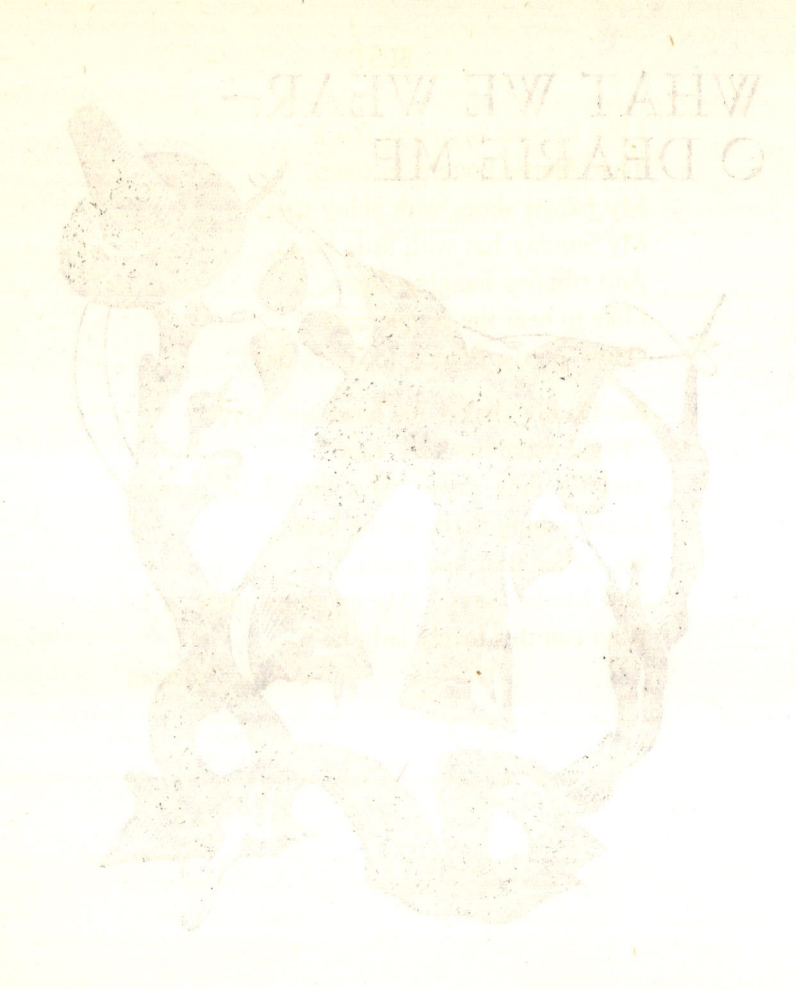

BEST

I like to wear my party frock
That Auntie bought in town,
My patent shoes with shiny toes,
My Sunday hat with little bows,
And ribbons hanging down.
I like to hear the people say:
"How pretty Nancy looks to-day!"

But Daddy shakes his head and says:
"You'll make her very vain."
And Grannie says: "She should be dressed
In everything that's of the best
But rather neat and plain."
And Mother says: "My goodness me!
Who *can* this lovely lady be?"
—*Rose Fyleman*

ELIZABETH ANN PEABODY[1]

The other day I went upstairs
   To our top attic-room;
'Twas dusty, dark and cobwebby,
   'Twas dim and full of gloom.
I lit a tall white candle there
   And in its flickering flame
I saw a dusty wooden chest,
   And, on the lid, a name.

"ELIZABETH ANN PEABODY"—
   Aloud I spelt it—so!
The name of Great-Great-Grandmama
   Who'd lived—oh, years ago!
I lifted up the heavy lid,
   It made a creaking sound,
And there inside, a silken dress,
   A crinoline, I found.

Beneath its folds there was a fan
   With rosy ribbons tied,
A pair of rosy mittens made
   Of lace was there beside.
I donned the blue-green crinoline,
   The lacy mittens too.
I looked inside the glass to see
   A face I scarcely knew.

It wasn't Betty Peabody
   Who looked right back at me!
It was—I'M CERTAIN—SHE!
   ELIZABETH ANN PEABODY!

[1] Taken from *Fairies and Suchlike*, by Ivy O. Eastwick, published and copyright, 1946, by E. P. Dutton & Co., Inc., New York.

Her hair was neatly parted
    In the sweetest little curls,
She looked the most demure of all
    Demure little girls.

She held the pretty fan with rosy
    Satin ribbons tied,
Her crinoline of blue-green billowed
    Out on either side.
Her mouth was red and smiling,
    And her shoulders pinky-pearl . . .
Oh, Elizabeth Ann Peabody,
    You were a charming girl!
            —Ivy O. Eastwick

THE MITTEN SONG

"Thumbs in the thumb-place,
Fingers all together!"
This is the song
We sing in mitten-weather.
When it is cold,
It doesn't matter whether
Mittens are wool,
Or made of finest leather.
This is the song
We sing in mitten-weather:
"Thumbs in the thumb-place,
Fingers all together!"
            —Marie Louise Allen

AN INDIGNANT MALE

The way they scrub
Me in the tub
I think there's
  Hardly
  Any
  Doubt
Sometime they'll rub
And rub and rub
Until they simply
  Rub
  Me
  Out.
    —*A. B. Ross*

MY ZIPPER SUIT

My zipper suit is bunny-brown—
The top zips up, the legs zip down.
I wear it every day.
My daddy brought it out from town.
Zip it up, and zip it down,
And hurry out to play.
    —*Marie Louise Allen*

BRYAN O'LIN HAD NO BREECHES TO WEAR

Bryan O'Lin had no breeches to wear,
So he bought him a sheepskin and made him a pair.
With the skinny side out, and the woolly side in,
"Ah ha, that is warm!" said Bryan O'Lin.
—*Mother Goose*

THE BONNIE CRAVAT

Jennie, come tie my,
Jennie, come tie my,
Jennie, come tie my bonnie cravat;
I've tied it behind,
I've tied it before,
I've tied it so often, I'll tie it no more.
—*Mother Goose*

BOBBY SHAFTOE'S GONE TO SEA

Bobby Shaftoe's gone to sea,
Silver buckles on his knee;
He'll come back and marry me,
Bonny Bobby Shaftoe!
Bobby Shaftoe's young and fair,
Combing down his yellow hair,
He's my love for evermore,
Bonny Bobby Shaftoe.
—*Mother Goose*

THE LOST SHOE

Poor little Lucy
  By some mischance,
Lost her shoe
  As she did dance:
'Twas not on the stairs
  Not in the hall;
Not where they sat
  At supper at all.
She looked in the garden,
  But there it was not;
Henhouse, or kennel,
  Or high dovecote.
Dairy and meadow,
  And wild woods through
Showed not a trace
  Of Lucy's shoe.
Bird nor bunny
  Nor glimmering moon
Breathed a whisper
  Of where 'twas gone.
It was cried and cried,
  Oyez and Oyez!
In French, Dutch, Latin,
  And Portuguese.
Ships the dark seas
  Went plunging through,
But none brought news
  Of Lucy's shoe;
And still she patters
  In silk and leather,
O'er snow, sand, shingle
  In every weather;

Spain, and Africa,
> Hindustan,
Java, China,
> And lamped Japan;
Plain and desert,
> She hops—hops through,
Pernambuco
> To gold Peru;
Mountain and forest,
> And river too,
All the world over
> For her lost shoe.
>> —*Walter de la Mare*

CHOOSING SHOES

New shoes, new shoes,
> Red and pink and blue shoes.
Tell me, what would *you* choose,
> If they'd let us buy?

Buckle shoes, bow shoes,
> Pretty pointy-toe shoes,
Strappy, cappy low shoes;
> Let's have some to try.

Bright shoes, white shoes,
> Dandy-dance-by-night shoes,
Perhaps-a-little-tight shoes,
> Like some? So would I.

> But

Flat shoes, fat shoes,
> Stump-along-like-that shoes,
Wipe-them-on-the-mat shoes,
That's the sort they'll buy.
>> —*ffrida Wolfe*

GALOSHES [1]

Susie's galoshes
Make splishes and sploshes
And slooshes and sloshes,
As Susie steps slowly
Along in the slush.

They stamp and they tramp
On the ice and concrete,
They get stuck in the muck and the mud;
But Susie likes much best to hear

The slippery slush
As it slooshes and sloshes,
And splishes and sploshes,
All round her galoshes!
    —Rhoda W. Bacmeister

HIGH AND LOW

A Boot and a Shoe and a Slipper
Lived once in a Cobbler's row;
 But the Boot and the Shoe
 Would have nothing to do
With the Slipper, because she was low.

But the king and the queen and their daughter
On the Cobbler chanced to call;
 And as neither the Boot
 Nor the Shoe would suit
The Slipper went off to the ball.
    —John Banister Tabb

[1] Taken from *Stories to Begin On*, by Rhoda W. Bacmeister, published and copyright, 1940, by E. P. Dutton & Co., Inc., New York.

COURTESY

A pretty little boy and a pretty little girl
   Found a pretty little blossom by the way;
Said the pretty little boy to the pretty little girl:
   "Take it, O my pretty one, I pray!"

Said the pretty little girl to the pretty little boy:
   "I must hold my Sunday bonnet, sir, you see:
So, I thank you very kindly, but I'd very much prefer
   You should carry it, and walk along with me."
                          —*Mary Mapes Dodge*

THE BUCKLE

I had a silver buckle,
I sewed it on my shoe,
And 'neath a sprig of mistletoe
I danced the evening through.

I had a bunch of cowslips,
I hid them in a grot,
In case the elves should come by night
And me remember not.

I had a yellow riband,
I tied it in my hair,
That, walking in the garden,
The birds might see it there.

I had a secret laughter,
I laughed it near the wall:
Only the ivy and the wind
May tell of it at all.
                —*Walter de la Mare*

POCKETS

A child should have a pocket—
   Supposing on the road
He runs across a beetle,
   Or a lizard, or a toad?
However will he carry them?
   Whatever will he do
If he hasn't got a pocket
   To put them into?

A child should have a pocket
   On which he fairly dotes!
Not one, or two, but many
   In his little waistcoats—
And one will be for money
   He finds on the roads,
And one for cake and cookies—
   And one for hoptoads!
      —*Susan Adger Williams*

COME, LET US PLAY

And dancing
And leaping
And laughing
We go!
   —Ivy O. Eastwick

ONE DAY WHEN WE WENT WALKING

One day when we went walking,
 I found a dragon's tooth,
 A dreadful dragon's tooth.
 "A locust thorn," said Ruth.

One day when we went walking,
 I found a brownie's shoe,
 A brownie's button shoe.
 "A dry pea pod," said Sue.

One day when we went walking,
 I found a mermaid's fan,
 A merry mermaid's fan.
 "A scallop shell," said Dan.

One day when we went walking,
 I found a fairy's dress,
 A fairy's flannel dress.
 "A mullein leaf," said Bess.

Next time that I go walking—
 Unless I meet an elf,
 A funny, friendly elf—
 I'm going by myself!
  —*Valine Hobbs*

THE PEAR TREE

I love our old pear tree,
Our old gnarled pear tree.
It doesn't bear apples
And it doesn't bear pears,
So it has lots of room
For the bears.

So up in the pear tree
Where the pears are not—
The nice juicy pears
That the tree hasn't got—
Lives a family of bears
As fierce as can be.

They're wild old bears
But they're scared of me.
'Cause whenever I shout
To the top of the tree,
"Bears, Bears,
You better watch out,
I'm coming up stairs—"

You can hear them growl,
The way bears do,
"Come on up stairs
We're not afraid of you."

But they're scared all right
'Cause they never stop
To play or fight.
When I reach the top
They're out of sight.

I wouldn't hurt the silly old bears.
I like them better than apples or pears
In our old pear tree
That doesn't grow apples
Or doesn't grow pears,
But leaves lots of room
For me and the bears.
—E. Elizabeth Longwell

GIRLS AND BOYS, COME OUT TO PLAY

Girls and boys, come out to play,
The moon doth shine as bright as day
Leave your supper, and leave your sleep,
And come with your playfellows into the street,
Come with a whoop, come with a call,
Come with a good will or not at all.
Up the ladder and down the wall,
A halfpenny roll will serve us all;
You find milk, and I'll find flour,
And we'll have a pudding in half-an-hour.
—Mother Goose

LITTLE CLOWN PUPPET

A little clown puppet began to fret,
"I'm tired of being a marionette . . ."

So he ran away and slept by a tree,

And while he was sleeping . . . Gracious me!
A crow came by on flapping wing
And picked him up for a ball of string.

She picked him up in her cawing beak,
But she let him drop when she heard him speak.

He fell through the air and caught on a limb,
And the earth was a long way off from him!
"Oh, dear, I shall never be free again!"

He wailed, and his tears fell fast as rain.
They fell on a chipmunk, brown and furry,
Who ran for a toadstool all in a hurry.

"Well," thought the puppet, "*that* is *cute*!
He thinks the stool is a bumbershoot.
Bring it up here," he called in glee,

"I'll use it to take me out of this tree."
So the chipmunk carried it up to him
Where he hung and swung on a crackling limb.

Then down from the tree the chipmunk scooted,
But the little clown puppet, he parachuted!
—*Carolyn Haywood*

SKATING

When I try to skate,
My feet are so wary
They grit and they grate;
And then I watch Mary
Easily gliding,
Like an ice-fairy;
Skimming and curving,
Out and in,
With a turn of her head,
And a lift of her chin,
And a gleam of her eye,
And a twirl and a spin;
Sailing under
The breathless hush
Of the willows, and back
To the frozen rush;
Out to the island
And round the edge,
Skirting the rim
Of the crackling sedge,
Swerving close
To the poplar root,
And round the lake
On a single foot,
With a three, and an eight,
And a loop and a ring;
Where Mary glides,
The lake will sing!
Out in the mist
I hear her now
Under the frost
Of the willow-bough

Easily sailing,
Light and fleet,
With the song of the lake
Beneath her feet.
  —Herbert Asquith

MERRY-GO-ROUND

I climbed up on the merry-go-round,
And it went round and round.

I climbed up on a big brown horse
And it went up and down.

 Around and round
 And up and down,
 Around and round
 And up and down,
 I sat high up
 On a big brown horse
 And rode around
 On the merry-go-round
  And rode around
 On the merry-go-round
  I rode around
 On the merry-go-round
  Around
   And round
    And
     Round.
  —Dorothy Walter Baruch

MY PLAN

When I'm a little older
   I plan to buy a boat,
And up and down the river
   The two of us will float.

I'll have a little cabin
   All painted white and red
With shutters for the window
   And curtains for the bed.

I'll have a little cookstove
   On which to fry my fishes,
And all the Hudson River
   In which to wash my dishes.
       —Marchette Chute

THE BIG SWING-TREE IS GREEN AGAIN

The big swing-tree is green again—
   That means that summer's coming;
If you listen, you may hear
   A pleasant sort of humming;
It sounds as if the big swing-tree
   Were chuckling low and singing,
And that's a happy sound, because
   It means we'll soon be swinging!
Up and up, down and down,
   Swinging high, swinging low,
All the children waiting turns,
   Standing in a row.
       —Mary Jane Carr

A SWING SONG

Swing, swing,
Sing, sing,
Here's my throne, and I am a king!
Swing, sing,
Swing, sing,
Farewell, Earth, for I'm on the wing!

Low, high,
Here I fly,
Like a bird through sunny sky;
Free, free,
Over the lea,
Over the mountain, over the sea!

Up, down,
Up and down,
Which is the way to London Town?
Where, where?
Up in the air,
Close your eyes, and now you are there!

Soon, soon,
Afternoon,
Over the sunset, over the moon;
Far, far,
Over all bar,
Sweeping on from star to star!

> No, no,
> Low, low,
> Sweeping daisies with my toe.
> Slow, slow,
> To and fro,
> Slow—
>   slow—
>   slow—
>   slow.
>   —*William Allingham*

THE HUT

We built a hut, my brother and I,
Over a sandy pit,
With twigs that bowed and met above
And leaves to cover it.

And there we sat when all around
The rain came pouring down.
We knew if we were out in it
We'd both be sure to drown.

And though in puddles at our feet
Drops gathered from the sky,
We smiled through strands of dripping hair,
Because we felt so dry.
    —*Hilda Van Stockum*

THE DRUM

The drum's a very quiet fellow
When he's left alone;
But oh, how he does roar and bellow,
Rattle, snap and groan,
Clatter, spatter, dash and patter,
Rumble, shriek and moan
Whene'er I take my sticks in hand
And beat him soundly for the band.
—*John Farrar*

THE HAYMOW

Up in the barn where they keep the hay
Is a wonderful, wonderful place to play.

So, "Who cares *that* if it starts to rain?"
Said Peter and Patrick, Samantha and Jane.

"Rain, rain, come and stay,
We're going out to the barn to play."

They tiptoed first to a knothole house
With a piece of cheese for their fav'rite mouse.

They found some kittens in a secret nest,
And the black hen setting where no one guessed.

They climbed where the rafters were dreadfully high,
And fell in the hay when they tried to fly.

They were castaways on a South Sea isle
And didn't get saved for a long, long while.

Then they thought up stories that were very clever,
And decided to live in the hay forever.

So they made deep tunnels in the soft sweet clover,
And there they lived—till the rain was over.
—*Luella Markley Mockett*

PIPINGS

Pipe thee high and pipe thee low!
Faster and faster small feet go,
Twinkling, dancing over the hill,
Little fat toes never keep still.

Pipe thee high and pipe thee low!
Red baby mouths sing so and so
To tripping tunes of green Pan pipes,
That lilt and fall o'er hay-cocked heights.

Pipe thee high and pipe thee low!
Grown-up people must dance just so;
But wee folk skip in sunlit lanes
As blossoms blow on window panes.
—*J. Paget-Fredericks*

GO DANCING TO SCHOOL

The sun's warm and friendly
The breeze soft and cool,
And gay little children
Go dancing to school.
          —Ivy O. Eastwick

MAY MORNINGS

May mornings are merry,
May mornings are gay,
For every green hedgerow
Is fragrant with may,
And every blithe blackbird
Is singing like mad,
And nothing is dreary
Or weary or sad.
The sun's warm and friendly,
The breeze soft and cool,
And gay little children
Go dancing to school.
—*Ivy O. Eastwick*

SCHOOL-BELL

Nine-o'clock Bell!
Nine-o'clock Bell!
All the small children and big ones as well,
Pulling their stockings up, snatching their hats,
Cheeking and grumbling and giving back-chats,
Laughing and quarreling, dropping their things,
These at a snail's pace and those upon wings,
Lagging behind a bit, running ahead,
Waiting at corners for lights to turn red,
    Some of them scurrying,
    Others not worrying,
Carelessly trudging or anxiously hurrying,
All through the streets they are coming pell-mell
    At the Nine-o'clock
        Nine-o'clock
        Nine-o'clock
            Bell!
—*Eleanor Farjeon*

SCHOOL BEGINS

What a gay
September day!
Chums meeting
Shout a greeting.
School bells clang,
"Hi ya, gang!"
—*Nell Goodale Price*

BEING SICK

Staying in bed and being sick
Is better as a rule
Than grammar or arithmetic
And other things at school.
—*Jimmy Garthwaite*

I'VE GOT A NEW BOOK FROM MY GRANDFATHER HYDE

I've got a new book from my Grandfather Hyde.
It's skin on the cover and paper inside,
And reads about Arabs and horses and slaves,
And tells how the Caliph of Bagdad behaves.
I'd not take a goat and a dollar beside
For the book that I got from my Grandfather Hyde.
—*Leroy F. Jackson*

ROGER FRANCIS

Roger Francis
   Isn't quick
At History dates
   Or Arithmetic;
But Roger Francis
   Is awfully fond
Of catching tiddlers
   In the pond.

The only date
   That ever I've
Known him recall
   Is November five;
The only Queen
   Quite clear in his head,
Is good Queen Anne
   (And he knows she's dead).

The only table
   He can recite,
Is the one times one
   (And not always right).
He knows that pennies
   His pocket filling,
Must count to twelve
   To be worth a shilling.

Roger Francis
   Never looks,
If he can help it,
   Inside of books;
Roger Francis
   Is happier far
With a rod, a net,
   And a pickle-jar.
      —*Wilfrid Thorley*

OUR HISTORY

Our history sings of centuries
Such varying songs it sings!
It starts with winds, slow moving sails,
It ends with skies and wings.
—*Catherine Cate Coblentz*

MULTIPLICATION IS VEXATION

Multiplication is vexation,
　Division is as bad;
The Rule of Three doth puzzle me,
　And Practice drives me mad.
—*Mother Goose*

GEOGRAPHY

Islands and peninsulas, continents and capes,
Dromedaries, cassowaries, elephants and apes,
Rivers, lakes and waterfalls, whirlpools and the sea,
Valley-beds and mountain-tops—are all Geography!

The capitals of Europe with so many curious names,
The North Pole and the South Pole and Vesuvius in flames,
Rice-fields, ice-fields, cotton-fields, fields of maize and tea,
The Equator and the Hemispheres—are all Geography!

The very streets I live in, and the meadows where I play,
Are just as much Geography as countries far away,
Where yellow girls and coffee boys are learning about me,
The little white-skinned stranger who is in Geography!
—*Eleanor Farjeon*

OLD MAPS

I love old maps made long ago
   With queer mistakes in foreign places,
Where all the things they didn't know
   Are empty spaces.

I love the pictures in the sea
   Of scaly dragons and of mermen
And monsters of dark mystery
   That used to stir men.

I love the men with tails, and those
   Whose head between their shoulders lingers,
The cannibals, those with no nose
   Or sixteen fingers.

I wish the maps we have in school
   Were not so dull, nor quite so finished.
I find my pleasure as a rule
   Is quite diminished.
                —*Eunice Tietjens*

THE ORGAN-GRINDER

The monkey and the organ man
   Come every now and then
They go away the longest time
   And then come back again.

They come around the school you know
   When we are out at noon
And play that hurdy gurdy thing
   That's *al*ways out of tune.

The monkey wears a velvet coat
   And asks you for a penny.
He asked me once—and squeaked at me
   Because I hadn't any!
        —*Jimmy Garthwaite*

SNIFF

When school is out, we love to follow
our noses over hill and hollow,
smelling jewelweed and vetch,
sniffing fern and milkweed patch.

The airy fifth of our five senses
leads us under, over, fences.
We run like rabbits through bright hours
and poke our noses into flowers!
        —*Frances Frost*

BELLS IN THE COUNTRY

Bells in the country,
   They sing the heart to rest
When night is on the high road
   And day is in the west.
               —Robert Nathan

BELLS IN THE COUNTRY

Bells in the country,
   They sing the heart to rest
When night is on the high road
   And day is in the west.

And once they came to my house
   As soft as beggars shod,
And brought it nearer heaven,
   And maybe nearer God.
            —*Robert Nathan*

CITY STREETS AND COUNTRY ROADS

The city has streets—
  But the country has roads.
In the country one meets
  Blue carts with their loads
Of sweet-smelling hay,
  And mangolds, and grain:
Oh, take me away
  To the country again!

In the city one sees,
  Big trams rattle by,
And the breath of the chimneys
  That blot out the sky,
And all down the pavements
  Stiff lamp-posts one sees—
But the country has hedgerows,
  The country has trees.

As sweet as the sun
  In the country is rain:
Oh, take me away
  To the country again!
      —*Eleanor Farjeon*

COUNTRY TRUCKS

Big trucks with apples
  And big trucks with grapes
Thundering through the mountains
  While every wild thing gapes.

Thundering through the valley,
    Like something just let loose,
Big trucks with oranges
    For city children's juice.

Big trucks with peaches,
    And big trucks with pears,
Frightening all the rabbits
    And giving squirrels gray hairs.

Yet, when city children
    Sit down to plum or prune,
They know more trucks are coming
    As surely as the moon.
                —*Monica Shannon*

MAD FARMER'S SONG

My father he left me three acres of land,
Sing ivy, sing ivy;
My father he left me three acres of land,
Sing holly, go whistle, and ivy!

I plowed it all with a ram's horn,
Sing ivy, sing ivy;
And sowed it all over with one pepper-corn,
Sing holly, go whistle, and ivy!

I harrowed it with a bramble bush,
Sing ivy, sing ivy;
And reaped it with my little penknife,
Sing holly, go whistle, and ivy!
                —*Author Unknown*

LEGACY

I had a rich old great-aunt
Who left me, when she died,
A little sloping acre
And not a thing beside.

Nothing else she left me
But a clump of sweet phlox
And an old silver aspen
And some hollyhocks.

A humming-bird disputed
My heritage with me,
And so did a robin
And a gold-backed bee.

A cricket owned a hummock,
He couldn't say how;
Two wrens held a mortgage
On one aspen bough.

A toad claimed a corner
(He said it was a lease).
We learned to live together
In a sort of cheery peace.

Never such an acre
To mortal was given!
My good old great-aunt,
May she rest in heaven!

—*Nancy Byrd Turner*

THE AXE HAS CUT THE FOREST DOWN

The axe has cut the forest down,
The laboring ox has smoothed all clear,
Apples now grow where pine trees stood,
And slow cows graze instead of deer.

Where Indian fires once raised their smoke
The chimneys of a farmhouse stand,
And cocks crow barnyard challenges
To dawns that once saw savage land.

The axe, the plow, the binding wall,
By these the wilderness is tamed,
By these the white man's will is wrought,
The rivers bridged, the new towns named.
—*Elizabeth Coatsworth*

EGGS

Bob has blown a hundred eggs,
Blue and olive, white and gray;
Warbler, nightingale, and thrush,
Bob has blown their songs away!

Low in spotless wool they rest,
Purest blue and clouded white,
Streaked with cinnamon and red,
Flecked with purples of the night:

Mute and gleaming, row on row,
Lie the tombstones of the spring!
What a chorus would there be,
If those eggs began to sing!
—*Herbert Asquith*

INQUISITIVE BARN

The white-housed village
In a feather bed
Sleeps with snow
About its head.

The only thing
In all this white
That keeps its lifting
Glow in sight

Is our old barn
That, loving fun,
Pokes its red head
Into the sun.
—*Frances Frost*

A LITTLE PIG ASLEEP

Behind Devaney's barn I saw
A little pig asleep.
His eyes were squiggened up so tight,
I'm sure he couldn't peep.

I crept right up beside him
And peeked 'way down his ear.
I'll bet he never even dreamed
A little boy was near.

His skin was full of bristles
From his forehead to his toes.
He had shellac on all his feet
And rubber on his nose.
—*Leroy F. Jackson*

FARM CART

The cart that carries hay,
The cart that carries corn,
Will carry you to church, my lass,
To-morrow in the morn.

There's sheep and little lambs
Has travelled in the cart,
And pigs has been its passengers
To and fro the mart.

Cordwood and oaken logs
It's carted from the wood
When woodman's axe have done its job
And felled the tree that stood.

Time my dad moved house
The cart have carried stools,
Tables, chairs, and kitchen things,
And beds, and garden tools.

Many and many a load
Have been the old cart's due,
But never have it borne, my lass,
So sweet a load as you.
  —Eleanor Farjeon

JACK SPRAT'S PIG

Jack Sprat's pig,
He was not very little,
Nor yet very big;
He was not very lean,
He was not very fat;
He'll do well for a grunt,
Says little Jack Sprat.
  —Mother Goose

RAKING WALNUTS IN THE RAIN

Mexican Jo and Mexican Jane
Rake down walnuts in the rain,
Rake them down when the jackets split—
Walnut jackets never fit!

Walnut jackets on the ground,
Perfectly green and perfectly round,
Walnuts in their under-shells
Clang together like distant bells.

Jo wears gingham for a coat,
Jane wears silk about her throat.
Flippity flop, her red skirt goes,
Through the dripping walnut rows.

Mexican Jo and Mexican Jane
Rake down walnuts in the rain,
Water running down their backs—
Steaming rakes and picking sacks!
—*Monica Shannon*

THE QUEST

Over crimson clover-seas
Let's go questing with the bees!
We shall find, where shores are sunny,
Such a golden store of honey!
—*Clinton Scollard*

BLOW, WIND, BLOW! AND GO, MILL, GO

Blow, wind, blow! And go, mill, go!
That the miller may grind his corn;
That the baker may take it,
And into rolls make it,
And send us some hot in the morn.
—*Mother Goose*

AUTUMN FIELDS

He said his legs were stiff and sore
For he had gone some twenty-eight miles,
And he'd walked through by water gaps
And fences and gates and stiles.

He said he'd been by Logan's woods,
And up by Walton's branch and Simms,
And there were sticktights on his clothes
And little dusts of seeds and stems.

And then he sat down on the steps,
And he said the miles were on his feet.
For some of that land was tangled brush,
And some was plowed for wheat.

The rabbits were thick where he had been,
And he said he'd found some ripe papaws.
He'd rested under a white oak tree,
And for his dinner he ate red haws.

Then I sat by him on the step
To see the things that he had seen.
And I could smell the shocks and clods,
And the land where he had been.
—*Elizabeth Madox Roberts*

THE HARVEST ELVES

The harvesters—they say themselves—
Are haunted by the harvest elves.

These elves—they say—as small as dolls
Have poppies for their parasols.

And when you hear the swish of stalks
It's elves a-sweeping their green walks.

And so when next a field you cross
And see the wheat-ears roll and toss,

Go quietly, and if you peep
Maybe you'll find an elf asleep

Inside a little hammock-bed,
Just as the harvesters have said.
—*Wilfrid Thorley*

THE RUNAWAY

Where did the little boy go, you say,
    Down through the garden gate?
He ran that way at half-past four,
    And you ponder upon his fate?

The phlox will make a friend of him,
    The rose, a captain tall,
And he will rout the wind that makes
    Their crimson petals fall.
The larkspur will cry out to him,
    "Bravo!" through merry hours,
Oh, do not weep for any lad
    Lost among the flowers!

You saw him sprinting down the lane
    Alone at half-past four—
And now 'tis six or thereabouts,
    No tidings at your door?

The butterflies will care for him,
    The Shasta daisies keep
Him safe within their silver fold;
    Nasturtium vines that creep
About the garden path will turn
    Him home ere darkness showers.
Oh, do not weep for any lad
    Lost among the flowers!

—Daniel Whitehead Hicky

THE DANDELION

O dandelion, rich and haughty,
King of village flowers!
Each day is coronation time,
You have no humble hours.
I like to see you bring a troop
To beat the blue-grass spears,
To scorn the lawn-mower that would be
Like fate's triumphant spears,
Your yellow heads are cut away,
It seems your reign is o'er.
By noon you raise a sea of stars
More golden than before.
—*Vachel Lindsay*

GROWING IN THE VALE

Growing in the vale
  By the uplands hilly,
Growing straight and frail,
  Lady Daffadowndilly.

In a golden crown,
And a scant green gown
  While the spring blows chilly,
Lady Daffadown,
  Sweet Daffadowndilly.
—*Christina G. Rossetti*

THE FOUR-LEAF CLOVER

"A four-leaf clover!" cried the Worm,
"The nicest place to sit and squirm!"

"A four-leaf clover!" croaked the Frog,
And nudged his little Pollywog.

"A four-leaf clover!" piped the Linnet,
"I'll make a nest and put this in it."

"A four-leaf clover!" said an Elf,
"Well, I can bring good luck myself;

"I know a lad who'd be a sailor,
I'll take him to an arctic whaler."

And now that lad is spearing whales,
Because he believed in fairy tales.
—*Monica Shannon*

QUEEN ANNE'S LACE

Queen Anne, Queen Anne, has washed her lace
  (She chose a summer's day)
And hung it in a grassy place
  To whiten, if it may.

Queen Anne, Queen Anne, has left it there,
  And slept the dewy night;
Then waked, to find the sunshine fair,
  And all the meadows white.

Queen Anne, Queen Anne, is dead and gone
  (She died a summer's day),
But left her lace to whiten on
  Each weed-entangled way!
—*Mary Leslie Newton*

FRINGED GENTIANS

Near where I live there is a lake
As blue as blue can be; winds make
It dance as they go blowing by.
I think it curtseys to the sky.

It's just a lake of lovely flowers,
And my Mamma says they are ours;
But they are not like those we grow
To be our very own, you know.

We have a splendid garden, there
Are lots of flowers everywhere;
Roses, and pinks, and four o'clocks,
And hollyhocks, and evening stocks.

Mamma lets us pick them, but never
Must we pick any gentians—ever!
For if we carried them away
They'd die of homesickness that day.
—*Amy Lowell*

A COMPARISON

Apple blossoms look like snow,
They're different, though.
Snow falls softly, but it brings
Noisy things:
Sleighs and bells, forts and fights,
Cosy nights.

But apple blossoms when they go,
White and slow,
Quiet all the orchard space,
Till the place
Hushed with falling sweetness seems
Filled with dreams.
—John Farrar

THE WILLOW CATS

They call them pussy willows,
   But there's no cat to see,
Except the little furry toes
   That stick out on the tree.

I think that very long ago
   When I was just born new,
There must have been whole pussy cats
   Where just the toes stick through.

And every spring it worries me,
   I cannot ever find
Those willow cats that ran away
   And left their toes behind!
—Margaret Widdemer

A LITTLE SONG OF LIFE

Glad that I live am I;
That the sky is blue;
Glad for the country lanes,
And the fall of dew.

After the sun the rain;
After the rain the sun;
This is the way of life,
Till the work be done.

All that we need to do,
Be we low or high,
Is to see that we grow
Nearer the sky.
—Lizette Woodworth Reese

THIS IS THE WONDROUS CITY

This is the wondrous city,
   Where worlds and nations **meet**;
Say not romance is napping;
   Behold the city street.
   —Morris Abel Beer

GOOD GREEN BUS

Rumbling and rattly good green Bus
Where are you going to carry us?
Up the shiny lengths of Avenue
Where lights keep company two by two;
Where windows glitter with things to buy,
And churches hold their steeples high.
Round the Circle and past the Park,
Still and shadowy, dim and dark,
Over the asphalt and into the Drive—
Isn't it fun to be alive?
Look to the left and the River's there
With ships and whistles and freshened air;
To the right—more windows, row on row,
And every one like a picture show,
Or little stages where people play
At being themselves by night and day,
And never guess that they have us
For audience in the good green Bus!
—Rachel Field

MRS. BARKS

On market days we always call
At Mrs. Barks's country stall.
Her bonnet is of white and blue,
She wears a coloured apron, too.
And she has baskets full of eggs
And fowls with neatly done up legs,
And butter too, and crinkly cheese
And sometimes plums or raspberries,
And gillyflowers in kitchen pots,
And bunches of forget-me-nots;
She also has a box of tin
For putting all her money in.
She has a very smiling face
And always stands there in her place
However wet the day may be
And says, "Good-morning, love," to me.
—*Rose Fyleman*

PUSHCART ROW

In rain or shine; in heat or snow;
The pushcarts stretch in a long green row,
Close to the curb as they can crowd,
With men all shouting their wares aloud.
If you have need of a lettuce head,
Or a bunch of radishes shiny red,
Of onions, carrots, or cauliflower,
Oranges sweet or lemons sour,
Polished apples or dripping greens,
Fat little mushrooms, thin string beans.
Of fruits and berries plump and round,
By the basket, by the pound—
Bring out your purse and take your pick
Where the two-wheeled pushcarts cluster thick;
Where dogs and children play about
Wheels and pavement and gutter-spout;
Where the women wear shawls and earrings gold,
And the men are mostly brown and old
With selling their wares in shine or snow
On the cobblestones of Pushcart Row.
—*Rachel Field*

WHO'LL BUY MY VALLEY LILIES?
STREET CHILD'S SONG

Who'll buy my valley lilies?
Who'll buy my scented gillies?
  All for a little money!
Who'll buy my daffydillies?

Who'll buy my blushing roses
For to delight their noses?
  All for a little money!
Who'll buy my scented posies?

They who buy rings and laces
For their fair hands and faces,
  All for a lot of money,
Yet will not buy such graces.

Who'll buy my valley lilies?
Who'll buy my scented gillies?
  All for a little money?
Who'll buy my daffydillies?
            —*Eleanor Farjeon*

FOOD

When I go walking down the street
There's lots of things I like to eat,

Like pretzels from the pretzel man
And buttered popcorn in a can,

And chocolate peppermints to lick
And candy apples on a stick.

Oh, there are many things to chew
While walking down the avenue.
            —*Marchette Chute*

THE GROCER AND THE GOLD-FISH

I'd asked the grocer
  For Cheddar cheese,
But cried out "O Sir,
  How much for *these*?"
For on his counter,
  As large as life,
Were a big gold-fish
  And his golden wife.

Wasn't it ripping!
  Among the bins
To find them flipping
  Their tails and fins?
Safe in their bowl
  With food all round,
Packet on packet,
  And pound on pound!

Said Mr. Melling,
  "Ev'n to *you*, Sir,
I'm not selling
  Sam nor Sue, Sir.
There they floats
  And feeds and kisses,
Gold-fish Sam
  And Sue his Mrs."

"I'm sorry, Sonny."
  (And so was I)
"But no-one's money
  Them fish won't buy."
So I lost my wish,
  For what is deader,
Compared with fish,
  Than a pound of Cheddar?
      —*Wilfrid Thorley*

THE POPCORN-POPPER

The popcorn man
At the park
Has a popping machine
Inside his cart.

   He puts in dry, yellow brown,
   Hard bits of corn
   And soon—
   Afaff afaff affafff—
   The corn begins to laugh
   And dance
   And hop
   And pop, and pop, and pop.

And then—
  I stand
  And hold
  The bag in my hand,
  And the man
  Pours it full
  Of puffy, fluffy, flaky,
  Soft white
    Popcorn.
      —*Dorothy Walter Baruch*

THE CITY AND THE TRUCKS

The city sleeps in its unconcern, but the highways are awake
With searching flashes and grinding gears and the hiss of air in a brake;
When darkness comes, like a roll of drums three million engines roar
Under throbbing hoods, and the nation's goods are out on the roads once more.

The city wakens to meet old needs and perhaps some new desires,
And finds the answer to all it asks brought in on the rubber tires:
There is coal and milk, there is rope and silk, there is shelter and food and dress
That lumbered in when the dawn was thin on the night highway express.

The city moves in its ordered round and never asks or knows
How drivers inch through the murky night as the fog-bank comes and goes,
How they breast the beat of the blinding sleet and shift for the slippery climb,
How they stop a fire, or tinker a tire—and pull into town on time!

The city takes, and it goes its way, and the great dark hulks re-load,
While mechanics grease, and test, and check, to make them safe for the road;
Then the crates are stacked and the boxes packed and the padding placed—and then
The tail-boards slam, and the trailers ram—and the great trucks roll again!

—Dorothy Brown Thompson

A MODERN BALLAD
THE UPS AND DOWNS OF THE ELEVATOR CAR

The elevator car in the elevator shaft,
Complained of the buzzer, complained of the draft.
It said it felt carsick as it rose and fell,
It said it had a headache from the ringing of the bell.

"There is spring in the air," sighed the elevator car.
Said the elevator man, "You are well-off where you are."
The car paid no attention but it frowned an ugly frown
```
                        when
              up                  it
          going              should
      started                       be
    it                                going
And                                     down.
```

Down flashed the signal, but *up* went the car.
The elevator man cried, "You are going much too far!"
Said the elevator car, "I'm doing no such thing.
I'm through with buzzers buzzing. I'm looking for the spring!"

Then the elevator man began to shout and call
And all the people came running through the hall.
The elevator man began to call and shout.
"The car won't stop! Let me out! Let me out!"

On went the car past the penthouse door.
On went the car up one flight more.
On went the elevator till it came to the top.
On went the elevator, and it would not stop!

Right through the roof went the man and the car.
And nobody knows where the two of them are!
(Nobody knows but everyone cares,
Wearily, drearily climbing the stairs!)

Now on a summer evening when you see a shooting star
Fly through the air, perhaps it *is*—that elevator car!
—Caroline D. Emerson

HUMP, THE ESCALATOR

Hump, the Escalator, slid
Out of the basement—yes, he did!
Out of the basement unawares,
Flattened a moment, then made a stairs;
Made a stairs that moved and crawled
Up through a runway, narrow-walled.

Here I stood on the floor below,
Then on a stair-step rising slow.
Over the heads of the shoppers then—
Dressed-up ladies and bothered men;

Over the aisles of hats and hose—
Over the shelf-displays I rose!
Suddenly stood on the second floor,
Not on a stairway any more.

Every rider ahead of me
Took it stiffly and solemnly.
Nobody paid a penny's fare—
Or knew they had ridden a Magic Stair!
—Dorothy Faubion

IT IS RAINING[1]

It is raining.

Where would you like to be in the rain?
Where would you like to be?

I'd like to be on a city street,
where the rain comes down in a driving sheet,
where it wets the houses—roof and wall—
the wagons and horses and autos and all.
That's where I'd like to be in the rain,
that's where I'd like to be.
—*Lucy Sprague Mitchell*

THE PARK

I'm glad that I
  Live near a park

For in the winter
  After dark

The park lights shine
  As bright and still

As dandelions
  On a hill.
—*James S. Tippett*

DAFFY-DOWN-DILLY

Daffy-down-dilly has come up to town,
In a yellow petticoat and a green gown.
—*Mother Goose*

---

[1] Taken from *Another Here and Now Story Book*, edited by Lucy Sprague Mitchell, published and copyright, 1937, by E. P. Dutton & Co., Inc., New York.

THE BELLS OF LONDON

*Gay go up and gay go down
To ring the bells of London town.*

Bull's-eyes and targets,
Say the bells of St. Marg'ret's.

Brick-bats and tiles,
Chime the bells of St. Giles'.

Halfpence and farthings,
Ring the bells of St. Martin's.

Oranges and lemons,
Toll the bells of St. Clement's.

Pancakes and fritters,
Say the bells of St. Peter's.

Two sticks and an apple,
Say the bells of Whitechapel.

Old Father Baldpate,
Toll the slow bells of Aldgate.

Pokers and tongs,
Say the bells at St. John's.

Kettles and pans,
Say the bells at St. Ann's.

You owe me ten shillings,
Say the bells of St. Helen's.

When will you pay me?
Say the bells of Old Bailey.

When I grow rich,
Chime the bells of Shoreditch.

Pray when will that be?
Ask the bells of Stepney.

I'm sure I don't know,
Tolls the great bell at Bow.

Gay go up and gay go down
To ring the bells of London town.
—Author Unknown

PARLIAMENT HILL

Have you seen the lights of London how they twinkle, twinkle, twinkle,
Yellow lights, and silver lights, and crimson lights, and blue?
And there among the other lights is Daddy's little lantern-light,
Bending like a finger-tip, and beckoning to you.

Never was so tall a hill for tiny feet to scramble up,
Never was so strange a world to baffle little eyes,
Half of it as black as ink with ghostly feet to fall on it,
And half of it all filled with lamps and cheerful sounds and cries.

Lamps in golden palaces, and station-lamps, and steamer-lamps,
Very nearly all the lamps that Mother ever knew,
And there among the other lamps is Daddy's little lantern-lamp
Bending like a finger-tip, and beckoning to you.
—H. H. Bashford

WHERE THE RED FOX HIDES

Where the red fox hides,
Why the nightingale sings. . . .
Dark Danny knows all
These lovely things.
—*Ivy O. Eastwick*

Taken from *Fairies and Suchlike*, by Ivy O. Eastwick, published and copyright, 1946, by E. P. Dutton & Co., Inc., New York.

DARK DANNY

Dark Danny has eyes
As black as the sloe,
And his freckles tell
Where the sunbeams go!

Dark Danny has hair
Like a raven's wing,
And his voice is gay
As the thrush in Spring.

Dark Danny will show
You the first wild rose;
Where the earliest violet
Blooms—he knows!

Where the red fox hides,
Why the nightingale sings. . . .
Dark Danny knows all
These lovely things.
   —*Ivy O. Eastwick*

CIRCUS ELEPHANT

Does the Elephant remember,
In the gray light before dawn,
Old noises of the jungle
In mornings long gone?

Does the Elephant remember
The cry of hungry beasts;
The Tiger and the Leopard,
The Lion at his feasts?

Do his mighty eardrums listen
For the thunder of the feet
Of the Buffalo and Zebra
In the dark and dreadful heat?

Does His Majesty remember,
Does he stir himself and dream
Of the long-forgotten music
Of a long-forgotten stream?

—*Kathryn Worth*

THE SPRING

A little mountain spring I found
That fell into a pool;
I made my hands into a cup
And caught the sparkling water up—
It tasted fresh and cool.

A solemn little frog I spied
Upon the rocky brim;
He looked so boldly in my face,
I'm certain that he thought the place
Belonged by rights to him.
—Rose Fyleman

RAMBUNCTIOUS BROOK

You should hear
our brook in Spring!
It is a noisy
tumbling thing.
It sneaks through thickets,
jumping out
to scare a beaver
with a shout!
It swoops round rocks
and laughs and pushes
the small green frogs
among its rushes,
who swell their silver
throats to song
and serenade it
all night long!
—Frances Frost

MICKLEHAM WAY[1]

A poor old woman,
Four score and a day,
She went a'walking
Mickleham way,
Basket on arm, and
Old gnarled stick in
Her old gnarled hand,
For blackberry pickin'.

But the woods were bare
Beyond the fen,
For the Mickleham women
And Mickleham men
And Mickleham children
Grave and gay,
Had gathered the blackberries
Mickleham way.

"Now woe is me,"
The old woman said,
"Better for me
If I were dead.
Seven long miles
Have I come, and now
There isn't a blackberry
Left, I vow!"

The dark, dry Bracken—
It heard! It heard!
The wild pink Foxgloves
With sorrow stirred!
They told the Wind

[1] Taken from *Fairies and Suchlike*, by Ivy O. Eastwick, published and copyright, 1946, by E. P. Dutton & Co., Inc., New York.

How matters stood—
Not a single blackberry
In the wood.

The Wind came down
To the Ancient Hills,
To the Little People
With Mighty Wills,
And told of the woman
Four score and a day
Who was sitting, weeping
Mickleham way.

And the Little People
With Mighty Wills
Left their homes
In the Ancient Hills;
They chanted a tune
That was old as earth
And held magic and pity
And tears and mirth.

The old, old woman,
She heard the sound,
Then saw the bushes
Bow down to the ground
And stay there, laden
At her feet
With blackberries large
And ripe and sweet.
—Ivy O. Eastwick

INDIAN PIPE AND MOCCASIN FLOWER

Indian pipe and moccasin flower
   Grow where the woodland waves,
Grow in the moss and the bracken bower
   Trod by the light-foot braves
Who played their part, who lived their hour
   And left, with a name that thrills,
Indian pipe and moccasin flower
   Scattered among our hills.
              —*Arthur Guiterman*

LAUGHING SONG

When the green woods laugh with the voice of joy,
And the dimpling stream runs laughing by;
When the air does laugh with our merry wit,
And the green hill laughs with the noise of it;

When the meadows laugh with lively green,
And the grasshopper laughs in the merry scene,
When Mary and Susan and Emily
With their sweet round mouths sing "Ha, Ha, He!"

When the painted birds laugh in the shade,
Where our table with cherries and nuts is spread,
Come live and be merry, and join with me,
To sing the sweet chorus of "Ha, Ha, He!"
              —*William Blake*

THE WEST WIND'S SECRET

Do you see that willow standing
    by the river there,
  Bending down its branches to the green waves
    below?

Do you think it's just a willow?
Oh, it never is a willow!
I know it's not a willow—
  For the West Wind told me so.

Will you promise not to tell it
    if I whisper in your ear?
For the West Wind surely wouldn't want
    just anyone to hear—

It's a princess, gently shaking
    out her golden hair,
  Looking at her image in the green waves below.

It's a fair, enchanted princess,
It's a lovely, lonely princess!
Oh, I know it is a princess—
  For the West Wind told me so.

—Mary Jane Carr

MIDSUMMER MAGIC[1]

Midsummer Eve, a year ago, my mother she commanded,
"Now don't you go a'running down to Ragwort Meadow!
And don't you go a'plucking of the bracken-seed or nightshade;
Stay out of the moonlight, mind! and keep out of the shadow,
   For they say that the Ragtag,
             Bobtail,
            Merry-derry
            Fairy-men
Tonight will go a'dancing down in Ragwort Meadow!"

Midsummer Eve, a year ago, my mother she commanded,
"Now don't you go a'playing down in Ragwort Meadow!
Keep away from thorn-tree, from adders' tongue and henbane!
Keep away from moonlight and don't venture in the shadow,
   For they say that the Ragtag,
            Bobtail,
           Merry-derry
           Fairy-men
Are out a'snaring mortals down in Ragwort Meadow."

I wouldn't heed my mother's words! I wouldn't heed her warning!
I ran through the moonlight, through the starlight and the shadow!
And I never stopped a'running though my breath came quick and
    gasping,
Till I reached the very middle of Ragwort Meadow,
   And there I heard the Ragtag,
           Bobtail,
           Merry-derry
           Fairy-men
A'laughing fit to kill themselves in Ragwort Meadow.

---

[1] Taken from *Fairies and Suchlike*, by Ivy O. Eastwick, published and copyright, 1946, by E. P. Dutton & Co., Inc., New York.

I heard 'em! But I couldn't see, no! not a little sight of 'em!
I pulled a curly bracken-leaf a'growing in the meadow,
I scratched out all the bracken-seeds and rubbed them on my eyelids—
The moon gave brilliant sunlight! There wasn't any shadow!
   And there I saw the Ragtag,
               Bobtail,
               Merry-derry
               Fairy-men
A'dancing round me in a ring in Ragwort Meadow.

Half-a-hundred fairy-men and half-a-score of rabbits;
Half-a-dozen squirrels down in Ragwort Meadow,
Dancing round me in a ring—you never saw the like of it!—
Underneath the daylight which the bright moon shed! Oh!
   A blessing on the Ragtag,
               Bobtail,
               Merry-derry
               Fairy-men
Who showed themselves to me down in Ragwort Meadow.

                    —*Ivy O. Eastwick*

BLESSED OF THE LORD BE HIS LAND

Blessed of the Lord be his land,
For the precious things of heaven, for the dew,
And for the deep that coucheth beneath,
And for the precious fruits brought forth by the sun,
And for the precious things put forth by the moon,
And for the chief things of the ancient mountains,
And for the precious things of the lasting hills,
And for the precious things of the earth and fullness thereof,
And for the good will of him that dwelt in the bush.
—*The Bible*

PIPPA'S SONG

The year's at the spring
And day's at the morn;
Morning's at seven;
The hill-side's dew-pearled;
The lark's on the wing;
The snail's on the thorn;
God's in his heaven—
All's right with the world.
—*Robert Browning*

DEEP IN THE SKY

The sky is full of star-dust,
It will be brighter soon;
An angel with a little cloud
Is dusting off the moon.
—*Abbie Farwell Brown*

WHEN A RING'S AROUND THE MOON

The wee folk will be tripping,
    In their silver dancing shoon,
Ring-around-the-meadow,
    When a ring's around the moon:

Curtsy to the right and left,
    And curtsy to the middle—
The fiddler will be fiddling
    On his tiny fairy fiddle;

In and out and round about,
    A magic circle making;
The pipers will be piping
    Till their tiny throats are aching.

Oh, few may watch the wee ones dance,
    For fairy guards are spying,
And down beneath the grasses
    All the dancers will be hieing;

But hearken well, what time you see
    A ring around the moon;
And you will hear the music
    Of the wee folks' dancing tune.

—*Mary Jane Carr*

MOCKERY

Happened that the moon was up before I went to bed,
Poking through the bramble trees her round gold head.
    I didn't stop for stocking,
I didn't stop for shoe,
But went running out to meet her—oh, the night was blue!

Barefoot down the hill road, dust beneath my toes;
Barefoot in the pasture smelling sweet of fern and rose!
    Oh, night was running with me,
Tame folk were all in bed—
And the moon was just showing her wild gold head.

But before I reached the hilltop where the bramble trees are tall,
I looked to see my lady moon—she wasn't there at all!—
    Not sitting on the hilltop,
Nor slipping through the air,
Nor hanging in the branches by her bright gold hair!

I walked slowly down the pasture and slowly up the hill,
Wondering and wondering, and very, very still.
    I wouldn't look behind me,
I went at once to bed—
And poking through the window was her bold gold head!

                    —*Katherine Dixon Riggs*

MOONBEAM

Moonbeam steps down the silken ladder
Woven by Mrs. Spider
To ask her to spin him a net
To catch the stars.
—Hilda Conkling

THE MOON'S THE NORTH WIND'S COOKY
WHAT THE LITTLE GIRL SAID

The Moon's the North Wind's cooky.
He bites it, day by day,
Until there's but a rim of scraps
That crumble all away.

The South Wind is a baker.
He kneads clouds in his den,
And bakes a crisp new moon that . . . *greedy*
North . . . Wind . . . eats . . . again!
—Vachel Lindsay

SILVER

Slowly, silently, now the moon
Walks the night in her silver shoon;
This way, and that, she peers, and sees
Silver fruit upon silver trees;
One by one the casements catch
Her beams beneath the silver thatch;
Couched in his kennel, like a log,
With paws of silver sleeps the dog;
From their shadowy cote the white breasts peep
Of doves in a silver-feathered sleep;
A harvest mouse goes scampering by,
With silver claws, and silver eye;
And moveless fish in the water gleam,
By silver reeds in a silver stream.
—*Walter de la Mare*

FULL MOON: SANTA BARBARA

I listened, there was not a sound to hear
   In the great rain of moonlight pouring down,
The eucalyptus trees were carved in silver,
   And a light mist of silver lulled the town.

I saw far off the grey Pacific bearing
   A broad white disk of flame,
And on the garden-walk a snail beside me
   Tracing in crystal the slow way he came.
—*Sara Teasdale*

NIGHT

Stars over snow,
  And in the west a planet
Swinging below a star—
  Look for a lovely thing and you will find it,
It is not far—
  It never will be far.
              —Sara Teasdale

STARS[1]

Bright stars, light stars
Shining-in-the-night stars,
Little twinkly, winkly stars,
Deep in the sky.

Yellow stars, red stars,
Shine-when-I'm-in-bed stars,
Oh how many blinky stars,
Far, far away!
        —Rhoda W. Bacmeister

THE FALLING STAR

I saw a star slide down the sky,
Blinding the north as it went by,
Too burning and too quick to hold,
Too lovely to be bought or sold,
Good only to make wishes on
And then forever to be gone.
            —Sara Teasdale

---

[1] Taken from *Stories to Begin On*, by Rhoda W. Bacmeister, published and copyright, 1940, by E. P. Dutton & Co., Inc., New York.

A CARAVAN FROM CHINA COMES

A caravan from China comes;
   For miles it sweetens all the air
With fragrant silks and dreaming gums,
   Attar and myrrh—
A caravan from China comes.

O merchant, tell me what you bring,
   With music sweet of camel bells;
How long have you been travelling
   With these sweet smells?
O merchant, tell me what you bring.

A lovely lady is my freight,
   A lock escaped of her long hair,—
That is this perfume delicate
   That fills the air—
A lovely lady is my freight.

Her face is from another land,
   I think she is no mortal maid,—
Her beauty, like some ghostly hand,
   Makes me afraid;
Her face is from another land.

The little moon my cargo is,
   About her neck the Pleiades
Clasp hands and sing: Hafiz, 'tis this
   Perfumes the breeze—
The little moon my cargo is.

                —*Richard Le Gallienne*

ESCAPE AT BEDTIME

The lights from the parlour and kitchen shone out
   Through the blinds and the windows and bars;
And high overhead and all moving about,
   There were thousands of millions of stars.
There ne'er were such thousands of leaves on a tree,
   Nor of people in church or the Park,
As the crowds of the stars that looked down upon me,
   And that glittered and winked in the dark.

The Dog, and the Plough, and the Hunter, and all,
   And the Star of the Sailor, and Mars,
These shone in the sky, and the pail by the wall
   Would be half full of water and stars.
They saw me at last, and they chased me with cries,
   And they soon had me packed into bed;
But the glory kept shining and bright in my eyes,
   And the stars going round in my head.
                    —Robert Louis Stevenson

DARKNESS

   The night is like an old cat
      out to hunt and kill;
   stealthy, black, greedy, fat,
      he slinks along the hill.

   The moon his eye, the stars his teeth,
      with long tail curled,
   he swallows city, farm and heath,
      his meal the whole world.
                —Peggy Bacon

CLOUDS

White sheep, white sheep,
On a blue hill,
When the wind stops
You all stand still
When the wind blows
You walk away slow.
White sheep, white sheep,
Where do you go?
—*Christina G. Rossetti*

BOATS SAIL ON THE RIVERS

Boats sail on the rivers,
   And ships sail on the seas;
But clouds that sail across the sky
   Are prettier far than these.

There are bridges on the rivers,
   As pretty as you please;
But the bow that bridges heaven,
   And overtops the trees,
And builds a road from earth to sky,
   Is prettier far than these.
—*Christina G. Rossetti*

I'LL TELL YOU HOW THE SUN ROSE

I'll tell you how the sun rose,—
A ribbon at a time.
The steeples swam in amethyst,
The news like squirrels ran.

The hills untied their bonnets,
The bobolinks begun.
Then I said softly to myself,
"That must have been the sun!"

*   *   *

But how he set, I know not.
There seemed a purple stile
Which little yellow boys and girls
Were climbing all the while,

Till when they reached the other side,
A dominie in gray
Put gently up the evening bars,
And led the flock away.
—Emily Dickinson

SKYWRITING

No feathered bird can weave
Pattern more perfect, pure,
Nor smoldering comet leave
A lovelier signature
Than they who in the sun
The vandal winds defy
And posters paste upon
The billboards of the sky.
—*Mary Maxtone*

HAPPY BE THE WEATHER

Something told the wild geese
It was time to fly,—
Summer sun was on their wings,
Winter in their cry.

—Rachel Field

SOMETHING TOLD THE WILD GEESE

Something told the wild geese
   It was time to go.
Though the fields lay golden
   Something whispered,—"Snow."
Leaves were green and stirring,
   Berries, luster-glossed,
But beneath warm feathers
   Something cautioned,—"Frost."
All the sagging orchards
   Steamed with amber spice,
But each wild breast stiffened
   At remembered ice.
Something told the wild geese
   It was time to fly,—
Summer sun was on their wings,
   Winter in their cry.

        —*Rachel Field*

WINDS A-BLOWING

The North Wind is a beggar
Who shudders at the cold.
The South Wind is a sailor
With pockets full of gold.
The East Wind is a gypsy
With saucy cap and feather.
The West Wind is a wizard
Who conjures wicked weather.

The Winter Wind's a giant
As grumpy as a bear.
The Summer Wind's a lady
With flowers in her hair.
The Autumn Wind's an old man
As touchy as a thistle.
The Spring Wind is a gay lad
Who blows a silver whistle.
—*May Justus*

WHO HAS SEEN THE WIND?

Who has seen the wind?
   Neither I nor you:
But when the leaves hang trembling
   The wind is passing thro'.

Who has seen the wind?
   Neither you nor I:
But when the trees bow down their heads
   The wind is passing by.
—*Christina G. Rossetti*

THE WIND

Who but the wind
Can follow his will:
To dream by the sea,
Or dance on a hill,
And master men's ships
As they cleave a green path?
Oh, the white waves thicken
At the smart of his wrath!
Who? oooh
The wind.

Who but the wind
Can leap over a steeple,
Or laughingly scatter
The hats of the people?
Or pass without footprint,
Or come without knock,
And herd the stray clouds
As a shepherd, his flock?
Who? oooh
The wind.

—Betty Miller

WHO LOVES THE RAIN

Who loves the rain,
   And loves his home,
And looks on life with quiet eyes,
   Him will I follow through the storm;
   And at his hearth-fire keep me warm;
Nor hell nor heaven shall that soul surprise,
   Who loves the rain,
   And loves his home,
And looks on life with quiet eyes.
               —*Frances Shaw*

APPLE SEASON

Come up in the orchard with grass to your knees,
for we're going shaking the apple trees!
The boughs are laden, bent low to the ground,
and the apples thud with a gentle sound.
Bright red, dark red, smooth and gold,
apples are sweet at the edge of cold!

Come up in the orchard with baskets now,
for we're going picking the apple bough!
Gather the firm bright globes of fire,
climb to the gnarled bough, climb up higher!
We're gathering apples with shout and song,
and we'll taste summer all winter long!
               —*Frances Frost*

PIRATE WIND

The autumn wind's a pirate,
    Blustering in from sea;
With a rollicking song, he sweeps along,
    Swaggering boist'rously.

His skin is weather-beaten;
    He wears a yellow sash,
With a handkerchief red about his head,
    And a bristling black mustache.

He laughs as he storms the country,
    A loud laugh and a bold;
And the trees all quake and shiver and shake,
    As he robs them of their gold.

The autumn wind's a pirate,
    Pillaging just for fun;
He'll snatch your hat as quick as that,
    And laugh to see you run!

—*Mary Jane Carr*

AUTUMN FIRES

In the other gardens
    And all up the vale,
From the autumn bonfires
    See the smoke trail!

Pleasant summer over
    And all the summer flowers,
The red fire blazes,
    The grey smoke towers.

Sing a song of seasons!
    Something bright in all!
Flowers in the summer,
    Fires in the fall!
      —*Robert Louis Stevenson*

NUTTING TIME

THUMP—THUD! Who is throwing
  Burrs and chestnuts to the ground?
Patter, scatter! Who is tossing
  Acorns, walnuts all around?

Come! Come! Bring your baskets,
  Search the ground, no need to climb,
Strong old North Wind from the branches
  Shakes the nuts; 'tis nutting time!
      —*Emilie Poulsson*

THE MIST AND ALL

I like the fall,
The mist and all.
I like the night owl's
Lonely call—
And wailing sound
Of wind around.

I like the gray
November day,
And bare, dead boughs
That coldly sway
Against my pane.
I like the rain.

I like to sit
And laugh at it—
And tend
My cozy fire a bit.
I like the fall—
The mist and all.—
   —Dixie Willson

OCTOBER'S PARTY

October gave a party;
    The leaves by hundreds came—
The Chestnuts, Oaks, and Maples,
    And leaves of every name.
The Sunshine spread a carpet,
    And everything was grand,
Miss Weather led the dancing,
    Professor Wind the Band.

The Chestnuts came in yellow,
    The Oaks in crimson dressed;
The lovely Misses Maple
    In scarlet looked their best;
All balanced to their partners,
    And gaily fluttered by;
The sight was like a rainbow
    New fallen from the sky.

Then, in the rustic hollow,
    At hide-and-seek they played,
The party closed at sundown,
    And everybody stayed.
Professor Wind played louder;
    They flew along the ground;
And then the party ended
    In jolly "hands around."
              —*George Cooper*

THRENODY

The red leaves fall upon the lake,
The brown leaves drift,
The yellow leaves fly with the wind,
High and swift.

The autumn nights bring open fires,
With roasted corn,
When silver frosted grasses greet
Early morn.

I fly my kite across the hill,
The slim string breaks,
It flashes like a cloud above
Hills and lakes.

I cannot follow, only stand
And watch it go,
Across the far and lonely place
That airplanes know.
—John Farrar

WHY DOES IT SNOW?

"Why does it snow? Why does it snow?"
The children come crowding around me to know.
I said to my nephew, I said to my niece,
"It's just the old woman a-plucking her geese."

    With her riddle cum dinky dido,
    With her riddle cum dinky dee.

The old woman sits on a pillowy cloud,
She calls to her geese, and they come in a crowd;
A cackle, a wackle, a hiss and a cluck,
And then the old woman begins for to pluck.

    With her riddle cum dinky dido,
    With her riddle cum dinky dee.

The feathers go fluttering up in the air,
Until the poor geese are entirely bare;
A toddle, a waddle, a hiss and a cluck,
"You may grow some more if you have the good luck!"

    With your riddle cum dinky dido,
    With your riddle cum dinky dee.

The feathers go swirling around and around,
Then whirlicking, twirlicking, sink to the ground;
The farther they travel, the colder they grow,
And when they get down here, they've turned into snow.

    With their riddle cum dinky dido,
    With their riddle cum dinky dee.
                —Laura E. Richards

THE FROST PANE

What's the good of breathing
On the window
Pane
In summer?
You can't make a frost
On the window pane
In summer.
You can't write a
Nalphabet
You can't draw a
Nelephant;
You can't make a smudge
With your nose
(In summer).

Lots of good, breathing
On the window
Pane
In winter.
You can make a frost
On the window pane
In winter.
A white frost, a light frost,
A thick frost, a quick frost,
A write-me-out-a-picture frost
Across
The pane
In
Winter.

—David McCord

A DEVONSHIRE RHYME

Walk fast in snow,
In frost walk slow,
And still as you go,
Tread on your toe.
When frost and snow are both together
Sit by the fire and spare shoe leather.
—*Author Unknown*

SLEET STORM

TIC-TIC-TIC!
The sound of the sleet
Fell like the beat
Of tiny feet,
Racing and chasing down the street:
The quick sharp beat
Of a million hoofs
Clicked and clattered
Across the roofs.
The sleet storm fell
Through a day and a night
With a tic-tic-tic
That was fast and light.

On the second morning
A cold sun shone
On a glittering, crystal,
Frigid zone.
Each bush and branch
Was icily hung
With the frozen song
The sleet had sung.

The branches swayed
With their icy load
Where millions of diamonds
Flashed and glowed.
Steep roofs shone
With a blinding glare.
Fringed with icicles
Everywhere.

But the tic-tic-tic
Of the sleet was still,
Caught on each glistening
Valley and hill.
—James S. Tippett

THAW

The snow is soft, and how it squashes!
"Galumph, galumph!" go my galoshes.
—Eunice Tietjens

KITE DAYS

A kite, a sky, and a good firm breeze,
And acres of ground away from trees,
And one hundred yards of clean, strong string—
O boy, O boy! I call that Spring!
—Mark Sawyer

SMELLS

Through all the frozen winter
My nose has grown most lonely
For lovely, lovely, colored smells
That come in springtime only.

The purple smell of lilacs,
The yellow smell that blows
Across the air of meadows
Where bright forsythia grows.

The tall pink smell of peach trees,
The low white smell of clover,
And everywhere the great green smell
Of grass the whole world over.
—Kathryn Worth

RAIN CLOUDS

Along a road
Not built by man
There winds a silent
Caravan
Of camel-clouds
Whose humped gray backs
Are weighted down
With heavy packs
Of long-awaited,
Precious rain
To make the old earth
Young again,
And dress her shabby
Fields and hills
In green grass silk
With wild-flower frills.
—Elizabeth-Ellen Long

RAIN MUSIC

On the dusty earth-drum
    Beats the falling rain;
Now a whispering murmur,
    Now a louder strain.

Slender silvery drumsticks,
    On the ancient drum,
Beat the mellow music,
    Bidding life to come.

Chords of earth awakened,
    Notes of greening spring,
Rise and fall triumphant
    Over everything.

Slender silvery drumsticks
    Beats the long tattoo—
God the Great Musician
    Calling life anew.
              —*Joseph S. Cotter, Jr.*

WHAT COULD BE LOVELIER THAN TO HEAR

What could be lovelier than to hear
The summer rain
Cutting across the heat, as scythes
Cut across grain?
Falling upon the steaming roof
With sweet uproar,
Tapping and rapping wildly
At the door?

No, do not go to lift the latch,
But through the pane
We'll stand and watch the circus pageant
Of the rain,
And see the lightning, like a tiger,
Striped and dread,
And hear the thunder cross the sky
With elephant tread.
—Elizabeth Coatsworth

THE SONG ON THE WAY

Any way the old world goes
    Happy be the weather!
With the red thorn or the rose
    Singin' all together!
Don't you see that sky o' blue?
    Good Lord painted it for you!
Reap the daisies in the dew
    Singin' all together!
Springtime sweet, an' frosty fall,
    Happy be the weather!
Earth has gardens for us all,
    Goin' on together.
Sweet the labor in the light,
    To the harvest's gold and white—
Till the toilers say "Good night,"
    Singin' all together!
             —*Author Unknown*

SHIPS AND SEAS

The sailor sings of ropes and things

In ships upon the seas.

—Robert Louis Stevenson

THE SEA SHELL

Sea Shell, Sea Shell,
   Sing me a song, O Please!
A song of ships, and sailormen,
   And parrots, and tropical trees,

Of islands lost in the Spanish Main
Which no man ever may find again,
Of fishes and corals under the waves,
And seahorses stabled in great green caves.

Sea Shell, Sea Shell,
Sing of the things you know so well.
         —*Amy Lowell*

SEA SHELLS

Oh, what do the sea shells murmur
   Again and yet again?
They tell of the little mer-maidens;
They tell of the little mer-men!
         —*Clinton Scollard*

THE MERMAIDENS

The little white mermaidens live in the sea,
In a palace of silver and gold;
And their neat little tails are all covered with scales,
Most beautiful for to behold.

On wild white horses they ride, they ride,
And in chairs of pink coral they sit;
They swim all the night, with a smile of delight,
And never feel tired a bit.
—*Laura E. Richards*

O SAILOR, COME ASHORE

O Sailor, come ashore,
   What have you brought for me?
Red coral, white coral,
   Coral from the sea.

I did not dig it from the ground,
   Nor pluck it from a tree;
Feeble insects made it
   In the stormy sea.
—*Christina G. Rossetti*

THIS IS THE HAY THAT NO MAN PLANTED

This is the hay that no man planted,
This is the ground that was never plowed,
Watered by tides, cold and brackish,
Shadowed by fog and the sea-born cloud.

Here comes no sound of bobolink's singing,
Only the wail of the gull's long cry,
Where men now reap as they reap their meadows
Heaping the great gold stacks to dry.

All winter long when deep pile the snowdrifts,
And cattle stand in the dark all day,
Many a cow shall taste pale sea-weed
Twined in the stalks of the wild salt hay.
—Elizabeth Coatsworth

THIS AIR THAT BLOWS IN FROM THE SEA

This air that blows in from the sea
No one has breathed before
Save only porpoises as they play
In waves far out from shore,
Or whales whose tranquil breathings rise
In fountains of white spray,
Or sailors leaning on the rails
Of ships from far away.

Sea gulls with nostrils of strong bone
Have tasted this keen breeze,
And gannets in their billowing flight,
But nothing less than these—
Nothing save creatures strong and wild
As vigorous and free,
Themselves, as is the wind that blows
So coldly from the sea.
—Elizabeth Coatsworth

THE FROWNING CLIFF

The sea has a laugh
And the cliff a frown;
For the laugh of the sea
Is wearing him down.

Lipping and lapping,
Frown as he may,
The laughing sea
Will eat him away;

Knees and body,
And tawny head,
He'll smile at last
On a golden bed.
—*Herbert Asquith*

SEA-WASH

The sea-wash never ends.
The sea-wash repeats, repeats.
Only old songs? Is that all the sea knows?
    Only the old strong songs?
  Is that all?
The sea-wash repeats, repeats.
—*Carl Sandburg*

A SHIP SAILS UP TO BIDEFORD

A ship sails up to Bideford;
Upon a western breeze
Mast by mast, sail over sail,
She rises from the seas,
And sights the hills of Devon
And the misty English trees.

She comes from Eastern islands;
The sun is in her hold;
She bears the fruit of Jaffa,
Dates, oranges and gold:

She brings the silk of China,
And bales of Persian dyes,
And birds with sparkling feathers,
And snakes with diamond eyes.

She's gliding in the starlight
As white as any gull:
The East is gliding with her
In shadows of her hull.

A ship sails up to Bideford,
Upon a western breeze,
With fruits of Eastern summers
She rises from the seas,
And sights the hills of Devon
And the misty English trees.
—*Herbert Asquith*

THE WIND HAS SUCH A RAINY SOUND

The wind has such a rainy sound
  Moaning through the town,
The sea has such a windy sound,—
  Will the ships go down?

The apples in the orchard
  Tumble from their tree.—
Oh will the ships go down, go down,
  In the windy sea?
      —Christina G. Rossetti

SEASCAPE

Off the coast of Ireland
As our ship passed by
We saw a line of fishing ships
Etched against the sky.

Off the coast of England
As we rode the foam
We saw an Indian merchantman
Coming home.
      —Langston Hughes

LOST

Desolate and lone
All night on the lake
Where fog trails and mist creeps,
The whistle of a boat
Calls and cries unendingly,
Like some lost child
In tears and trouble
Hunting the harbor's breast
And the harbor's eyes.
—*Carl Sandburg*

FREIGHT BOATS

Boats that carry sugar
And tobacco from Havana;
Boats that carry cocoanuts
And coffee from Brazil;
Boats that carry cotton
From the city of Savannah;
Boats that carry anything
From any place you will.

Boats like boxes loaded down
With tons of sand and gravel;
Boats with blocks of granite
For a building on the hill;
Boats that measure many thousand
Lonesome miles of travel
As they carry anything
From any place you will.

—James S. Tippett

THE STORM SNAPPED ITS FINGERS

The storm snapped its fingers—
"Ship, are you afraid?
Now's the time, my pretty one,
To show how you were made!

"Were your timbers seasoned,
Built of chosen wood?
And your sheathing honest?
And your canvas good?

"Did the men who made you
Build with careful thought?
Dream each line and ponder
When your hull was wrought?"

The storm rent sky and ocean—
"Ship, are you afraid?
Now's the time, my little bird,
To prove how you were made!"

—Elizabeth Coatsworth

WHITE HORSES

Little white horses are out on the sea,
   Bridled with rainbows and speckled with foam,
Laden with presents for you and for me;
   Mermaids and fairies are riding them home!
          Gold from the sun;
          Diamonds rare
          Made from dew
          And frosty air;
          Veils of mist,
          Soft and white,
          Rose and silver,
          Shimmering, bright;
          Sweetest perfumes,
          Coloured shells,
          Lilting music,
          Fairy bells:
Fairies and mermaids are bringing them home
On Little White Horses all speckled with foam.
                  —*Winifred Howard*

WHO PILOTS SHIPS

Who pilots ships knows all a heart can know
Of beauty, and his eyes may close in death
And be content. There is no wind to blow
Whiter than foam-white wind and no wind's breath
Sweeter than tropic wind. There is no star
That throbs with cold white fire as North stars do,
No golden moon-path lovelier than the far
Path burning on the sea when dusk is blue.
There is no rain so swift as rain that flies
In bright battalions with a storm begun,
No song that shakes the heart like amber cries
Of gulls with wing turned yellow in the sun.
Who pilots ships, when life's last heartbeats stop,
Has drained the cup of beauty drop by drop.
—*Daniel Whitehead Hicky*

JOLLY DAYS

Jolly days, holidays

Have come round again.

—*Ivy O. Eastwick*

Taken from *Fairies and Suchlike*, by Ivy O. Eastwick, published and copyright, 1946, by E. P. Dutton & Co., Inc., New York.

THE NEW YEAR

Who comes dancing over the snow,
His soft little feet all bare and rosy?
Open the door though the wild winds blow,
Take the child in and make him cozy.
Take him in and hold him dear,
He is the wonderful glad New Year.
—Dinah M. Mulock Craik

I'LL WEAR A SHAMROCK

St. Patrick's day is with us,
   The day when all that's seen
To right and left and everywhere
   Is green, green, green!

And Irish tunes they whistle
   And Irish songs they sing,
To-day each Irish lad walks out
   As proud as any king.

I'll wear a four-leaf shamrock
   In my coat, the glad day through,
For my father and mother are Irish
   And I am Irish, too!
—Mary Carolyn Davies

EASTER IN THE WOODS

This dawn when the mountain-cherry lifts
its frail white bloom among dark pines,
and chipmunks flash small happy paws
along old tumbled boundary lines,
this golden morning when the vixen
nuzzles her five young foxes forth
to roll in ferns in the Easter sun,—
again the woods know soft green birth.

Snuffed by a puffball infant rabbit
are yellow violets by the spring;
among half-opened apple buds
a wood thrush tilts his head to sing.
Risen is He! And they are His,
who scamper under warm blue skies,
who nibble little fists of grass,
and gaze on earth with shy glad eyes.
—*Frances Frost*

EASTER PARADE

My button gloves are very white,
   My parasol is new,
My braids are braided nice and tight,
   And there are very few
Of all the people that I see
Who are as beautiful as me.
—*Marchette Chute*

CHOICE

If I had just one penny
  On the Fourth of July,
Oh, what a problem it would be
  To think what I should buy!

With lollypops and fire-works,
  With cakes and whiz-bangs, too,
With tops and candy cigarettes,
  Whatever should I do?

Torpedoes have a splendid noise,
  But noise is quickly past,
And the sweetness of a lollypop
  Is something that will last.
            —*John Farrar*

THIS IS HALLOWEEN

Goblins on the doorstep,
   Phantoms in the air,
Owls on witches' gateposts
   Giving stare for stare,
Cats on flying broomsticks,
   Bats against the moon,
Stirrings round of fate-cakes
   With a solemn spoon,
Whirling apple parings,
   Figures draped in sheets
Dodging, disappearing,
   Up and down the streets,
Jack-o'-lanterns grinning,
   Shadows on a screen,
Shrieks and starts and laughter—
   This is Halloween!
          —Dorothy Brown Thompson

THANKSGIVING MAGIC

Thanksgiving Day I like to see
Our cook perform her witchery.
She turns a pumpkin into pie
As easily as you or I
Can wave a hand or wink an eye.
She takes leftover bread and muffin
And changes them to turkey stuffin'.
She changes cranberries to sauce
And meats to stews and stews to broths;
And when she mixes gingerbread
It turns into a man instead
With frosting collar 'round his throat
And raisin buttons down his coat.
Oh, some like magic made by wands,
   And some read magic out of books,
And some like fairy spells and charms
   But I like magic made by cooks!
               —*Rowena Bastin Bennett*

CHRISTMAS GREETING

Sing hey! Sing hey!
For Christmas Day;
Twine mistletoe and holly,
For friendship glows
In winter snows,
And so let's all be jolly.
—*Author Unknown*

BUT GIVE ME HOLLY, BOLD AND JOLLY

But give me holly, bold and jolly,
Honest, prickly, shining holly;
Pluck me holly leaf and berry
For the day when I make merry.
—*Christina G. Rossetti*

THE CHRISTMAS EXCHANGE

When Bill gives me a book, I know
It's just the book he wanted, so
When I give him a ping-pong set,
He's sure it's what I hoped to get.

Then after Christmas we arrange
A little Christmas Gift Exchange;
I give the book to him, and he
Gives back the ping-pong set to me.

So each gives twice—and that is pleasant—
To get the truly-wanted present.
—*Arthur Guiterman*

BUNDLES

A bundle is a funny thing,
It always sets me wondering;
For whether it is thin or wide
You never know just what's inside.

Especially on Christmas week,
Temptation is so great to peek!
Now wouldn't it be much more fun
If shoppers carried things undone?
—*John Farrar*

PRESENTS

I wanted a rifle for Christmas
I wanted a bat and a ball,
I wanted some skates and a bicycle,
But I didn't want mittens at all.

I wanted a whistle
And I wanted a kite,
I wanted a pocketknife
That shut up tight.
I wanted some books
And I wanted a kit,
But I didn't want mittens one little bit.

I told them I didn't like mittens,
I told them as plain as plain.
I told them I didn't WANT mittens
And they've given me mittens again!
—*Marchette Chute*

CHRISTMAS

My goodness, my goodness,
It's Christmas again.
The bells are all ringing.
I do not know when
I've been so excited.
The tree is all fixed,
The candles are lighted,
The pudding is mixed.
The wreath's on the door
And the carols are sung,
The presents are wrapped
And the holly is hung.
The turkey is sitting
All safe in its pan,
And I am behaving
As calm as I can.
—Marchette Chute

MY GIFT

What can I give Him
Poor as I am;
If I were a shepherd,
I would give Him a lamb.
If I were a wise man,
I would do my part.
But what can I give Him?
I will give Him my heart.
—Christina G. Rossetti

WORDS FROM AN OLD SPANISH CAROL

Shall I tell you who will come
   to Bethlehem on Christmas Morn,
who will kneel them gently down
   before the Lord, new-born?

One small fish from the river,
   with scales of red, red gold,
one wild bee from the heather,
   one grey lamb from the fold,
one ox from the high pasture,
   one black bull from the herd,
one goatling from the far hills,
   one white, white bird.

And many children—God give them grace,
bringing tall candles to light Mary's face.

Shall I tell you who will come
   to Bethlehem on Christmas Morn,
who will kneel them gently down
   before the Lord, new-born?
           —Ruth Sawyer, trans.

LONG, LONG AGO

Winds through the olive trees
    Softly did blow,
Round little Bethlehem
    Long, long ago.

Sheep on the hillside lay
    Whiter than snow;
Shepherds were watching them,
    Long, long ago.

Then from the happy sky,
    Angels bent low,
Singing their songs of joy,
    Long, long ago.

For in a manger bed,
    Cradled we know,
Christ came to Bethlehem,
    Long, long ago.
        —*Author Unknown*

ABOVE THE STABLE

Above the stable,
    Angels sing,
Inside the manger
    Lies a King!

Lies an Infant,
    Meek and lowly
Lies a Sovereign
    High and Holy!
        —*Nona Keen Duffy*

CHRISTMAS IN THE WOODS

Tonight when the hoar frost falls on the wood,
And the rabbit cowers, and the squirrel is cold,
And the horned owl huddles against a star,
And the drifts are deep, and the year is old,
All shy creatures will think of Him.
The shivering mouse, the hare, the wild young fox,
The doe with the startled fawn,
Will dream of gentleness and a Child:

The buck with budding horns will turn
His starry eyes to a silver hill tonight,
The chipmunk will awake and stir
And leave his burrow for the chill, dark midnight,
And all timid things will pause and sigh, and sighing, bless
That Child who loves the trembling hearts,
The shy hearts of the wilderness.
—*Frances Frost*

CHRISTMAS CAROL

God bless the master of this house,
    The mistress also,
And all the little children,
    That round the table go,
And all your kin and kinsmen
    That dwell both far and near;
I wish you a Merry Christmas
And a Happy New Year.
           —*Author Unknown*

A LITTLE HOUSE WILL PLEASE

Sometimes a little house will please
The heart a mansion cannot win.
It seems to curtsy by the door
To ask you in.

—Elizabeth Coatsworth

SOMETIMES A LITTLE HOUSE WILL PLEASE

Sometimes a little house will please
The heart a mansion cannot win.
It seems to curtsy by the door
To ask you in.

So bright shine all the windowpanes,
So fresh the little rooms and gay,
The kettle bobbing on the stove
Asks you to stay.

It tries to tell you things it knew
Of captains and the fishing fleet,
Of summer calms and winter gales,
Of wind and sleet.

It tries to tell you of the wives
And children living, waiting there—
"Bad days and good, good days and bad,"
Creaks the small rocking chair.

—Elizabeth Coatsworth

OUR HOUSE

Our house is small—
The lawn and all
Can scarcely hold the flowers,
Yet every bit,
The whole of it,
Is precious, for it's ours!

From door to door,
From roof to roof,
From wall to wall we love it;
We wouldn't change
For something strange
One shabby corner of it!

The space complete
In cubic feet
From cellar floor to rafter
Just measures right,
And not too tight,
For us, and friends, and laughter!
—Dorothy Brown Thompson

THE LITTLE BIRD

My dear Daddie bought a mansion
  For to bring my Mammie to,
In a hat with a long feather,
  And a trailing gown of blue;
And a company of fiddlers
  And a rout of maids and men
Danced the clock round to the morning,
  In a gay house-warming then.
And when all the guests were gone, and
  All was still as still can be,
In from the dark ivy hopped a
  Wee small bird: and that was Me.
        —*Walter de la Mare*

OLD LOG HOUSE

On a little green knoll
At the edge of the wood
My great great grandmother's
First house stood.

The house was of logs
My grandmother said
With one big room
And a lean-to shed.

The logs were cut
And the house was raised
By pioneer men
In the olden days.

I like to hear
My grandmother tell
How they built the fireplace
And dug the well.

They split the shingles;
They filled each chink;
It's a house of which
I like to think.

Forever and ever
I wish I could
Live in a house
At the edge of a wood.
—James S. Tippett

I LIKE HOUSE CLEANING

It's fun to clean house.
  The food isn't much,
And paint's all about
  That we mustn't touch;
But strange stored-away things,
Not like everyday things,
Make marvelous playthings
  From attics and such.

The boxes come out
  From closets and chests,
With odd sorts of clothes
  Like old hats and vests,
And photographed faces,
And ribbons and laces,
And postcards of places,
  And cards left by guests.

Then Mother says, "Throw
  The whole lot away!"
And Father says, "Wait—
  I'll need this someday."
But either way's meaning
A chance to go gleaning
Among the house cleaning
  For new things to play!
          —Dorothy Brown Thompson

CROSS PATCH

Cross patch,
Draw the latch,
Sit by the fire and spin;
Take a cup,
And drink it up,
Then call your neighbors in.
—*Mother Goose*

THE CASTLE IN THE FIRE

The andirons were the dragons,
　Set out to guard the gate
Of the old enchanted castle,
　In the fire upon the grate.

We saw a turret window
　Open a little space,
And frame, for just a moment,
　A lady's lovely face;

Then, while we watched in wonder
　From out the smoky veil,
A gallant knight came riding,
　Dressed in coat of mail;

With slender lance a-tilting,
　Thrusting with a skillful might,
He charged the crouching dragons—
　Ah, 'twas a brilliant fight!

Then, in the roar and tumult,
　The back log crashed in two,
And castle, knight and dragons
　Were hidden from our view;

But, when the smoke had lifted,
  We saw, to our delight,
Riding away together,
  The lady and the knight.
           —*Mary Jane Carr*

A WORD ABOUT WOODPILES

Life isn't dreary,
  Nor altogether hard,
If one has a woodpile
  In one's back yard:

Chips like a carpet,
  Sweet bark rolled,
Little knots of lightwood
  Worth their weight in gold;

Cedar slabs fragrant
  In the golden sun;
Pine sticks stewing
  When the rosin starts to run;

Logs of oak and chestnut,
  Logs of beech and birch;
And a sort of clear quiet,
  Like the quiet in a church,

And a kind of homey comfort
  That warms to the core—
There's nothing like a woodpile
  At one's back door!
           —*Nancy Byrd Turner*

AT MRS. APPLEBY'S

When frost is shining on the trees,
   It's spring at Mrs. Appleby's.
You smell it in the air before
   You step inside the kitchen door.

Rows of scarlet flowers bloom
   From every window in the room.
And funny little speckled fish
   Are swimming in a china dish.

A tiny bird with yellow wings
   Just sits and sings and sings and SINGS.
Outside when frost is on the trees,
   It's spring at Mrs. Appleby's!
       —Elizabeth Upham McWebb

GODMOTHER

There was an old lady
Who had three faces,
One for everyday,
And one for wearing places—
To meetings and parties,
Dull places like that—
A face that looked well
With a grown-up hat.

But she carried in her pocket
The face of an elf,
And she'd clap it on quick
When she felt like herself.
Sitting in the parlor
Of somebody's house,
She'd reach in her pocket
Sly as a mouse . . .
And there in the corner,
Sipping her tea,
Was a laughing elf-woman
Nobody could see!
—Phyllis B. Morden

BIBLE STORIES

The room was low and small and kind;
   And in its cupboard old,
The shells were set out to my mind;
   The cups I loved with rims of gold.

Then, with that good gift which she had,
   My mother showed at will,
David, the ruddy Syrian lad,
   With his few sheep upon a hill;

A shop down a rude country street,
   The chips strewn on the floor,
And faintly keen across the heat;
   The simple kinsfolk at the door;

Mary amid the homely din,
   As slim as violet;
The little Jesus just within,
   About His father's business set.

My mother rose, and then I knew
   As she stood smiling there,
Her gown was of that gentle blue
   Which she had made the Virgin wear.

How far the very chairs were grown!
   The gilt rose on each back,
Into a Syrian rose was blown,
   And not our humble gold and black.

That week long, in our acres old,
   Lad David did I see;
From out our cups with rims of gold,
   The little Jesus supped with me.
             —*Lizette Woodworth Reese*

THE LITTLE CARVED BOWL

I always wanted
   A little carved bowl
With grapes around the edges
   And gilt on the whole
And a daffodil garden
   And a singing soul;

I wanted gold rings
   And a satin dress
And a friend who knew
   What no other could guess
And a very great
   Gold happiness. . . .

I never have had
   The satin gown
And no gold happiness
   Ever came down
To be my shelter
   And my shining crown,

Nor a daffodil garden
   Nor a singing soul
Nor ever a friend
   Who knew me whole
But today someone gave me
   A little carved bowl.
           —*Margaret Widdemer*

WHO'S IN

"The door is shut fast
And everyone's out."
But people don't know
What they're talking about!
Says the fly on the wall,
And the flame on the coals,
And the dog on his rug,
And the mice in their holes,
And the kitten curled up,
And the spiders that spin—
"What, everyone's out?
Why, everyone's in!"
—Elizabeth Fleming

HOUSE BLESSING [1]

Bless the four corners of this house,
   And be the lintel blest;
And bless the hearth and bless the board
   And bless each place of rest;
And bless the door that opens wide
   To stranger as to kin;
And bless each crystal window-pane
   That lets the starlight in;
And bless the rooftree overhead
   And every sturdy wall.
The peace of man, the peace of God,
   The peace of Love on all!
—Arthur Guiterman

[1] Taken from *Death and General Putnam and 101 Other Poems*, by Arthur Guiterman, published and copyright, 1935, by E. P. Dutton & Co., Inc., New York.

A CHILD'S GRACE

Some hae meat and canna eat,
   And some wad eat that want it;
But we hae meat and we can eat,
   And sae the Lord be thankit.
        —*Robert Burns*

WHEN JACKY'S A VERY GOOD BOY

When Jacky's a very good boy,
He shall have cakes and a custard;
But when he does nothing but cry,
He shall have nothing but mustard.
        —*Mother Goose*

NOSE, NOSE, JOLLY RED NOSE

Nose, nose, jolly red nose;
And what gave thee that jolly red nose?
Nutmegs and cinnamon, spices and cloves,
And they gave me this jolly red nose.
        —*Mother Goose*

POLLY PUT THE KETTLE ON

Polly put the kettle on,
Polly put the kettle on,
Polly put the kettle on,
   And let's drink tea.
        —*Mother Goose*

THE CUPBOARD

I know a little cupboard,
With a teeny tiny key,
And there's a jar of Lollypops
    For me, me, me.

It has a little shelf, my dear,
As dark as dark can be,
And there's a dish of Banbury Cakes
    For me, me, me.

I have a small fat grandmamma,
With a very slippery knee,
And she's Keeper of the Cupboard,
    With the key, key, key.

And when I'm very good, my dear,
As good as good can be,
There's Banbury Cakes, and Lollypops
    For me, me, me.

—Walter de la Mare

TURTLE SOUP

Beautiful Soup, so rich and green,
Waiting in a hot tureen!
Who for such dainties would not stoop?
Soup of the evening, beautiful Soup!
Soup of the evening, beautiful Soup!
    Beau—ootiful Soo—oop!
    Beau—ootiful Soo—oop!
Soo—oop of the e—e—evening,
    Beautiful, beautiful Soup!

Beautiful Soup! Who cares for fish,
Game, or any other dish?
Who would not give all else for two p
   ennyworth only of beautiful Soup?
Pennyworth only of beautiful Soup?
    Beau—ootiful Soo—oop!
    Beau—ootiful Soo—oop!
Soo—oop of the e—e—evening,
    Beautiful, beauti—FUL SOUP!
       —Lewis Carroll

WASH THE DISHES, WIPE THE DISHES

Wash the dishes, wipe the dishes,
Ring the bell for tea;
Three good wishes, three good kisses,
I will give to thee.
       —Mother Goose

MAGIC LARIAT

We went to a circus in the town
And saw a cowboy lasso a clown.
Then, reaching home through the late sunshine,
We made a lariat out of a vine
And tried to whirl it about and cling
To posts, each other, or anything
That pleased our fancy. . . . That must **be**
The reason we had chanced to see,
At the garden's edge, a silvery thread,
Like a magic lariat over the head
Of a marigold just opened that day,
From a little bare bush across the way—
A cobweb noose flung out to hold
A moment that had turned to gold!
—*Glenn Ward Dresbach*

OF A SPIDER

The spider weaves his silver wire
Between the cherry and the brier.

He runs along and sees the thread
Well-fastened on each hawser-head.

And then within his wheel he dozes
Hung on a thorny stem of roses,

While fairies ride the silver ferry
Between the rose-bud and the cherry.
—*Wilfrid Thorley*

MISTRESS MARY, QUITE CONTRARY

Mistress Mary, quite contrary
  How does your garden grow?
With cockle-shells, and silver bells,
  And pretty maids all in a row.

PROUD HOLLYHOCK

The hollyhock with crimson bells
  Has grown so proudly high
It leans atop the garden wall
  To see what it can spy.

It sees our neighbor, Mrs. Maggs,
  A-hanging out the clothes:
The winding road and distant fields
  Where corn is stacked in rows.

But never, never does it see
  The wonders in the grass,
Where under tiny spears of jade
  The tiny insects pass. . . .
          —*Marguerite Buller*

NIGHT WATCHMEN

When I'm in bed at night,
   Outside my door
And just in sight
At the head of the stairs
Sit two little bears.

They sit very still,
   As still as can be.
They're sitting on guard,
   Just watching, you see.

Their ears are wide open,
   And so are their eyes.
They'll catch anyone
   If anyone tries
To come up the stairs.
But nobody dares
Because of the bears!
     —*Wymond Garthwaite*

DEEDLE, DEEDLE, DUMPLING, MY SON JOHN

Deedle, deedle, dumpling, my son John,
Went to bed with his stockings on;
One shoe off, and one shoe on,
Deedle, deedle, dumpling, my son John.
         —*Mother Goose*

SHOP OF DREAMS

Shop of dreams is up on a hill,
   Close to the morning star;
An odd little shop, in a meadow of sleep,
   Where all kinds of novelties are.

Just follow the road to Slumberland,
   That leads over hill and dale,
And right at the end you will see a sign:
"Very Fine Dreams For Sale."

The keeper of dreams is an old, old man,
   With a twinkle in his eye—
He's been showing his wares since the world was new,
   To people who come to buy;

Tucked under the eaves, small drowsy birds
   Sing slumber songs, over and over,
While wooly white sheep jump over the fence
   To nibble the moonbeam clover.

—Mary Jane Carr

CRADLE SONG

From groves of spice,
O'er fields of rice,
Athwart the lotus-stream,
I bring for you,
Aglint with dew,
A little lovely dream.

Sweet, shut your eyes,
The wild fire-flies
Dance through the fairy *neem*;
From the poppy-bole
For you I stole
A little lovely dream.

Dear eyes, good night,
In golden light
The stars around you gleam;
On you I press
With soft caress
A little lovely dream.
—*Sarojini Naidu*

GOOD NIGHT [1]

On tip-toe comes the gentle dark
To help the children sleep
And silently, in silver paths,
The slumber fairies creep.

Then overhead, God sees that all
His candles are a-light,
And reaching loving arms to us
He bids His world Good Night.
—*Dorothy Mason Pierce*

---

[1] Taken from *The Susianna Winkle Book*, by Dorothy Mason Pierce, published and copyright, 1935, by E. P. Dutton & Co., Inc., New York.

INDEX OF AUTHORS

ALLEN, MARIE LOUISE
   The Mitten Song, 19
   My Zipper Suit, 20
ALLINGHAM, WILLIAM
   A Swing Song, 36
ASQUITH, HERBERT
   Eggs, 55
   The Frowning Cliff, 131
   A Ship Sails up to Bideford, 132
   Skating, 33
AUTHOR UNKNOWN
   The Bells of London, 79
   Christmas Carol, 152
   Christmas Greeting, 146
   A Devonshire Rhyme, 118
   Long, Long Ago, 150
   Mad Farmer's Song, 53
   The Railroad Cars Are Coming, 7
   The Song on the Way, 124

BACMEISTER, RHODA W.
   Galoshes, 24
   Stars, 99
BACON, PEGGY
   Darkness, 101
BARUCH, DOROTHY WALTER
   Merry-Go-Round, 34
   The Popcorn-Popper, 74
BASHFORD, H. H.
   Parliament Hill, 80
BENNETT, ROWENA BASTIN
   Thanksgiving Magic, 145
BIBLE
   Blessed of the Lord Be His Land, 92
BLAKE, WILLIAM
   Laughing Song, 88

BROWNING, ROBERT
   Pippa's Song, 92
BULLER, MARGUERITE
   Proud Hollyhock, 171
BURNS, ROBERT
   A Child's Grace, 167

CARR, MARY JANE
   The Big Swing-Tree Is Green Again, 35
   The Castle in the Fire, 160
   Pirate Wind, 111
   Shop of Dreams, 173
   The West Wind's Secret, 89
   When a Ring's Around the Moon, 95
CARROLL, LEWIS
   Turtle Soup, 169
CHUTE, MARCHETTE
   Christmas, 148
   Easter Parade, 142
   Food, 72
   My Plan, 35
   Presents, 147
COATSWORTH, ELIZABETH
   The Axe Has Cut the Forest Down, 55
   Sometimes a Little House Will Please, 155
   The Storm Snapped Its Fingers, 136
   This Air That Blows in from the Sea, 130
   This Is the Hay That No Man Planted, 129
   What Could Be Lovelier Than to Hear, 123

COBLENTZ, CATHERINE CATE
  Our History, 46
CONKLING, HILDA
  Moonbeam, 97
COOPER, GEORGE
  October's Party, 114
COTTER, JOSEPH S., JR.
  Rain Music, 122
CRAIK, DINAH M. MULOCK
  The New Year, 141

DAVIES, MARY CAROLYN
  I'll Wear a Shamrock, 141
DE LA MARE, WALTER
  The Buckle, 25
  The Cupboard, 168
  The Little Bird, 157
  The Lost Shoe, 22
  Silver, 98
  Somewhere, 13
DICKINSON, EMILY
  I'll Tell You How the Sun Rose, 103
DODGE, MARY MAPES
  Courtesy, 25
DRESBACH, GLENN WARD
  Magic Lariat, 170
DUFFY, NONA KEEN
  Above the Stable, 150

EASTWICK, IVY O.
  Dark Danny, 83
  Elizabeth Ann Peabody, 18
  May Mornings, 43
  Mickleham Way, 86
  Midsummer Magic, 90
EMERSON, CAROLINE D.
  A Modern Ballad (The Ups and Downs of the Elevator Car), 76

FARJEON, ELEANOR
  City Streets and Country Roads, 52
  Farm Cart, 57
  Geography, 46
  Sailor, 9
  School-Bell, 43
  Who'll Buy My Valley Lilies?, 72
FARRAR, JOHN
  Bundles, 147
  Choice, 143
  A Comparison, 65
  The Drum, 38
  Threnody, 115
FAUBION, DOROTHY
  Hump, the Escalator, 77
FIELD, RACHEL
  Good Green Bus, 69
  If Once You Have Slept on an Island, 11
  Pushcart Row, 71
  Roads, 3
  Something Told the Wild Geese, 107
FLEMING, ELIZABETH
  Who's In, 166
FROST, FRANCES
  Apple Season, 110
  Christmas in the Woods, 151
  Easter in the Woods, 142
  Inquisitive Barn, 56
  Rambunctious Brook, 85
  Sniff, 48
  Trains at Night, 7
FYLEMAN, ROSE
  The Barge, 10
  Best, 17
  The Boat, 10

Mrs. Barks, 70
The Spring, 85

GARTHWAITE, JIMMY
Being Sick, 44
The Organ-Grinder, 48
GARTHWAITE, WYMOND
Night Watchmen, 172
GUITERMAN, ARTHUR
The Christmas Exchange, 146
House Blessing, 166
Indian Pipe and Moccasin Flower, 88

HAYWOOD, CAROLYN
Little Clown Puppet, 32
HICKY, DANIEL WHITEHEAD
The Runaway, 61
Who Pilots Ships, 138
HOBBS, VALINE
One Day When We Went Walking, 29
HOWARD, WINIFRED
White Horses, 137
HUGHES, LANGSTON
Seascape, 133

JACKSON, LEROY F.
All Aboard for Bombay, 8
I've Got a New Book from My Grandfather Hyde, 44
A Little Pig Asleep, 56
JUSTUS, MAY
Winds A-Blowing, 108

LE GALLIENNE, RICHARD
A Caravan from China Comes, 100

LINDSAY, VACHEL
The Dandelion, 62
The Moon's the North Wind's Cooky, 97
LONG, ELIZABETH-ELLEN
Rain Clouds, 121
LONGWELL, E. ELIZABETH
The Pear Tree, 30
LOWELL, AMY
Fringed Gentians, 64
The Sea Shell, 127

MCCORD, DAVID
The Frost Pane, 117
MCWEBB, ELIZABETH UPHAM
At Mrs. Appleby's, 162
MAXTONE, MARY
Skywriting, 104
MILLER, BETTY
The Wind, 109
MITCHELL, LUCY SPRAGUE
It Is Raining, 78
MOCKETT, LUELLA MARKLEY
The Haymow, 39
MORDEN, PHYLLIS B.
Godmother, 163
MOTHER GOOSE
Blow, Wind, Blow! And Go, Mill, Go, 59
Bobby Shaftoe's Gone to Sea, 21
The Bonnie Cravat, 21
Bryan O'Lin Had No Breeches to Wear, 21
Cross Patch, 160
Daffy-Down-Dilly, 78
Deedle, Deedle, Dumpling, My Son John, 172
Girls and Boys, Come Out to Play, 31

Jack Sprat's Pig, 57
Mistress Mary, Quite Contrary, 171
Multiplication Is Vexation, 46
Nose, Nose, Jolly Red Nose, 167
Polly Put the Kettle On, 167
Wash the Dishes, Wipe the Dishes, 169
When Jacky's a Very Good Boy, 167

NAIDU, SAROJINI
Cradle Song, 174
NATHAN, ROBERT
Bells in the Country, 51
NEWTON, MARY LESLIE
Queen Anne's Lace, 63
PAGET-FREDERICKS, J.
Pipings, 40
PIERCE, DOROTHY MASON
Good Night, 174
POULSSON, EMILIE
Nutting Time, 112
PRICE, NELL GOODALE
School Begins, 44
REESE, LIZETTE WOODWORTH
Bible Stories, 164
A Little Song of Life, 66
RICHARDS, LAURA E.
The Mermaidens, 128
Why Does It Snow?, 116
RIGGS, KATHERINE DIXON
Mockery, 96
ROBERTS, ELIZABETH MADOX
Autumn Fields, 59
ROSS, A. B.
An Indignant Male, 20
ROSSETTI, CHRISTINA G.
Boats Sail on the Rivers, 102

But Give Me Holly, Bold and Jolly, 146
Clouds, 102
Growing in the Vale, 62
My Gift, 148
O Sailor, Come Ashore, 128
Who Has Seen the Wind?, 108
The Wind Has Such a Rainy Sound, 133

SANDBURG, CARL
Lost, 134
Sea-Wash, 131
SAWYER, MARK
Kite Days, 119
SAWYER, RUTH
Words from an Old Spanish Carol, 149
SCOLLARD, CLINTON
The Quest, 58
Sea Shells, 127
SHANNON, MONICA
Country Trucks, 52
The Four-Leaf Clover, 63
Raking Walnuts in the Rain, 58
SHAW, FRANCES
Who Loves the Rain, 110
STEVENSON, ROBERT LOUIS
Autumn Fires, 112
Escape at Bedtime, 101

TABB, JOHN BANISTER
High and Low, 24
TEASDALE, SARA
The Falling Star, 99
Full Moon: Santa Barbara, 98
Night, 99
THOMPSON, DOROTHY BROWN
The City and the Trucks, 75

I Like House Cleaning, 159
Maps, 6
Our House, 156
This Is Halloween, 144
THORLEY, WILFRID
    The Grocer and the Gold-Fish, 73
    The Harvest Elves, 60
    Of a Spider, 170
    The Old Inn-Sign, 4
    Roger Francis, 45
TIETJENS, EUNICE
    Old Maps, 47
    Thaw, 119
TIPPETT, JAMES S.
    Freight Boats, 135
    Old Log House, 158
    The Park, 78
    Sleet Storm, 118
TURNER, NANCY BYRD
    Legacy, 54
    A Word About Woodpiles, 161

VAN STOCKUM, HILDA
    The Hut, 37
WIDDEMER, MARGARET
    The Little Carved Bowl, 165
    The Willow Cats, 65
WILLIAMS, SUSAN ADGER
    Pockets, 26
WILLSON, DIXIE
    The Mist and All, 113
WOLFE, FFRIDA
    Choosing Shoes, 23
WORTH, KATHRYN
    Circus Elephant, 84
    Smells, 120

YOUNG, BARBARA
    Being a Gypsy, 12
    Road Fellows, 5
YOUNGS, MARY FANNY
    The Edge of the World, 8

INDEX OF TITLES

Above the Stable, by NONA KEEN DUFFY	150
All Aboard for Bombay, by LEROY F. JACKSON	8
Apple Season, by FRANCES FROST	110
At Mrs. Appleby's, by ELIZABETH UPHAM MCWEBB	162
Autumn Fields, by ELIZABETH MADOX ROBERTS	59
Autumn Fires, by ROBERT LOUIS STEVENSON	112
Axe Has Cut the Forest Down, The, by ELIZABETH COATSWORTH	55
Barge, The, by ROSE FYLEMAN	10
Being a Gypsy, by BARBARA YOUNG	12
Being Sick, by JIMMY GARTHWAITE	44
Bells in the Country, by ROBERT NATHAN	51
Bells of London, The, AUTHOR UNKNOWN	79
Best, by ROSE FYLEMAN	17
Bible Stories, by LIZETTE WOODWORTH REESE	164
Big Swing-Tree Is Green Again, The, by MARY JANE CARR	35
Blessed of the Lord Be His Land, THE BIBLE	92
Blow, Wind, Blow! And Go, Mill, Go, MOTHER GOOSE	59
Boat, The, by ROSE FYLEMAN	10
Boats Sail on the Rivers, by CHRISTINA G. ROSSETTI	102
Bobby Shaftoe's Gone to Sea, MOTHER GOOSE	21
Bonnie Cravat, The, MOTHER GOOSE	21
Bryan O'Lin Had No Breeches to Wear, MOTHER GOOSE	21
Buckle, The, by WALTER DE LA MARE	25
Bundles, by JOHN FARRAR	147
But Give Me Holly, Bold and Jolly, by CHRISTINA G. ROSSETTI	146
Caravan from China Comes, A, by RICHARD LE GALLIENNE	100
Castle in the Fire, The, by MARY JANE CARR	160
Child's Grace, A, by ROBERT BURNS	167
Choice, by JOHN FARRAR	143
Choosing Shoes, by FFRIDA WOLFE	23
Christmas, by MARCHETTE CHUTE	148
Christmas Carol, AUTHOR UNKNOWN	152
Christmas Exchange, The, by ARTHUR GUITERMAN	146

Christmas Greeting, AUTHOR UNKNOWN	146
Christmas in the Woods, by FRANCES FROST	151
Circus Elephant, by KATHRYN WORTH	84
City and the Trucks, The, by DOROTHY BROWN THOMPSON	75
City Streets and Country Roads, by ELEANOR FARJEON	52
Clouds, by CHRISTINA G. ROSSETTI	102
Comparison, A, by JOHN FARRAR	65
Country Trucks, by MONICA SHANNON	52
Courtesy, by MARY MAPES DODGE	25
Cradle Song, by SAROJINI NAIDU	174
Cross Patch, MOTHER GOOSE	160
Cupboard, The, by WALTER DE LA MARE	168
Daffy-Down-Dilly, MOTHER GOOSE	78
Dandelion, The, by VACHEL LINDSAY	62
Dark Danny, by IVY O. EASTWICK	83
Darkness, by PEGGY BACON	101
Deedle, Deedle, Dumpling, My Son John, MOTHER GOOSE	172
Devonshire Rhyme, A, AUTHOR UNKNOWN	118
Drum, The, by JOHN FARRAR	38
Easter in the Woods, by FRANCES FROST	142
Easter Parade, by MARCHETTE CHUTE	142
Edge of the World, The, by MARY FANNY YOUNGS	8
Eggs, by HERBERT ASQUITH	55
Elizabeth Ann Peabody, by IVY O. EASTWICK	18
Escape at Bedtime, by ROBERT LOUIS STEVENSON	101
Falling Star, The, by SARA TEASDALE	99
Farm Cart, by ELEANOR FARJEON	57
Food, by MARCHETTE CHUTE	72
Four-Leaf Clover, The, by MONICA SHANNON	63
Freight Boats, by JAMES S. TIPPETT	135
Fringed Gentians, by AMY LOWELL	64
Frost Pane, The, by DAVID MCCORD	117
Frowning Cliff, The, by HERBERT ASQUITH	131
Full Moon: Santa Barbara, by SARA TEASDALE	98
	181

Galoshes, by RHODA W. BACMEISTER	24
Geography, by ELEANOR FARJEON	46
Girls and Boys, Come Out to Play, MOTHER GOOSE	31
Godmother, by PHYLLIS B. MORDEN	163
Good Green Bus, by RACHEL FIELD	69
Good Night, by DOROTHY MASON PIERCE	174
Grocer and the Gold-Fish, The, by WILFRID THORLEY	73
Growing in the Vale, by CHRISTINA G. ROSSETTI	62
Harvest Elves, The, by WILFRID THORLEY	60
Haymow, The, by LUELLA MARKLEY MOCKETT	39
High and Low, by JOHN BANISTER TABB	24
House Blessing, by ARTHUR GUITERMAN	166
Hump, the Escalator, by DOROTHY FAUBION	77
Hut, The, by HILDA VAN STOCKUM	37
I Like House Cleaning, by DOROTHY BROWN THOMPSON	159
If Once You Have Slept on an Island, by RACHEL FIELD	11
I'll Tell You How the Sun Rose, by EMILY DICKINSON	103
I'll Wear a Shamrock, by MARY CAROLYN DAVIES	141
Indian Pipe and Moccasin Flower, by ARTHUR GUITERMAN	88
Indignant Male, An, by A. B. ROSS	20
Inquisitive Barn, by FRANCES FROST	56
It Is Raining, by LUCY SPRAGUE MITCHELL	78
I've Got a New Book from My Grandfather Hyde, by LEROY F. JACKSON	44
Jack Sprat's Pig, MOTHER GOOSE	57
Kite Days, by MARK SAWYER	119
Laughing Song, by WILLIAM BLAKE	88
Legacy, by NANCY BYRD TURNER	54
Little Bird, The, by WALTER DE LA MARE	157
Little Carved Bowl, The, by MARGARET WIDDEMER	165
Little Clown Puppet, by CAROLYN HAYWOOD	32
Little Pig Asleep, A, by LEROY F. JACKSON	56

182

Little Song of Life, A, by LIZETTE WOODWORTH REESE	66
Long, Long Ago, AUTHOR UNKNOWN	150
Lost, by CARL SANDBURG	134
Lost Shoe, The, by WALTER DE LA MARE	22
Magic Lariat, by GLENN WARD DRESBACH	170
Mad Farmer's Song, AUTHOR UNKNOWN	53
Maps, by DOROTHY BROWN THOMPSON	6
May Mornings, by IVY O. EASTWICK	43
Mermaidens, The, by LAURA E. RICHARDS	128
Merry-Go-Round, by DOROTHY WALTER BARUCH	34
Mickleham Way, by IVY O. EASTWICK	86
Midsummer Magic, by IVY O. EASTWICK	90
Mist and All, The, by DIXIE WILLSON	113
Mistress Mary, Quite Contrary, MOTHER GOOSE	171
Mitten Song, The, by MARIE LOUISE ALLEN	19
Mockery, by KATHERINE DIXON RIGGS	96
Modern Ballad, A (The Ups and Downs of the Elevator Car), by CAROLINE D. EMERSON	76
Moonbeam, by HILDA CONKLING	97
Moon's the North Wind's Cooky, The, by VACHEL LINDSAY	97
Mrs. Barks, by ROSE FYLEMAN	70
Multiplication Is Vexation, MOTHER GOOSE	46
My Gift, by CHRISTINA G. ROSSETTI	148
My Plan, by MARCHETTE CHUTE	35
My Zipper Suit, by MARIE LOUISE ALLEN	20
New Year, The, by DINAH M. MULOCK CRAIK	141
Night, by SARA TEASDALE	99
Night Watchmen, by WYMOND GARTHWAITE	172
Nose, Nose, Jolly Red Nose, MOTHER GOOSE	167
Nutting Time, by EMILIE POULSSON	112
O Sailor, Come Ashore, by CHRISTINA G. ROSSETTI	128
October's Party, by GEORGE COOPER	114
Of a Spider, by WILFRID THORLEY	170
Old Inn-Sign, The, by WILFRID THORLEY	4

Old Log House, by JAMES S. TIPPETT	158
Old Maps, by EUNICE TIETJENS	47
One Day When We Went Walking, by VALINE HOBBS	29
Organ-Grinder, The, by JIMMY GARTHWAITE	48
Our History, by CATHERINE CATE COBLENTZ	46
Our House, by DOROTHY BROWN THOMPSON	156
Park, The, by JAMES S. TIPPETT	78
Parliament Hill, by H. H. BASHFORD	80
Pear Tree, The, by E. ELIZABETH LONGWELL	30
Pipings, by J. PAGET-FREDERICKS	40
Pippa's Song, by ROBERT BROWNING	92
Pirate Wind, by MARY JANE CARR	111
Pockets, by SUSAN ADGER WILLIAMS	26
Polly Put the Kettle On, MOTHER GOOSE	167
Poporn-Popper, The, by DOROTHY WALTER BARUCH	74
Presents, by MARCHETTE CHUTE	147
Proud Hollyhock, by MARGUERITE BULLER	171
Pushcart Row, by RACHEL FIELD	71
Queen Anne's Lace, by MARY LESLIE NEWTON	63
Quest, The, by CLINTON SCOLLARD	58
Railroad Cars Are Coming, The, AUTHOR UNKNOWN	7
Rain Clouds, by ELIZABETH-ELLEN LONG	121
Rain Music, by JOSEPH S. COTTER, JR.	122
Raking Walnuts in the Rain, by MONICA SHANNON	58
Rambunctious Brook, by FRANCES FROST	85
Road Fellows, by BARBARA YOUNG	5
Roads, by RACHEL FIELD	3
Roger Francis, by WILFRID THORLEY	45
Runaway, The, by DANIEL WHITEHEAD HICKY	61
Sailor, by ELEANOR FARJEON	9
School Begins, by NELL GOODALE PRICE	44
School-Bell, by ELEANOR FARJEON	43
Sea Shell, The, by AMY LOWELL	127

Sea Shells, by CLINTON SCOLLARD	127
Sea-Wash, by CARL SANDBURG	131
Seascape, by LANGSTON HUGHES	133
Ship Sails up to Bideford, A, by HERBERT ASQUITH	132
Shop of Dreams, by MARY JANE CARR	173
Silver, by WALTER DE LA MARE	98
Skating, by HERBERT ASQUITH	33
Skywriting, by MARY MAXTONE	104
Sleet Storm, by JAMES S. TIPPETT	118
Smells, by KATHRYN WORTH	120
Sniff, by FRANCES FROST	48
Something Told the Wild Geese, by RACHEL FIELD	107
Sometimes a Little House Will Please, by ELIZABETH COATSWORTH	155
Somewhere, by WALTER DE LA MARE	13
Song on the Way, The, AUTHOR UNKNOWN	124
Spring, The, by ROSE FYLEMAN	85
Stars, by RHODA W. BACMEISTER	99
Storm Snapped Its Fingers, The, by ELIZABETH COATSWORTH	136
Swing Song, A, by WILLIAM ALLINGHAM	36
Thanksgiving Magic, by ROWENA BASTIN BENNETT	145
Thaw, by EUNICE TIETJENS	119
This Air That Blows in from the Sea, by ELIZABETH COATSWORTH	130
This Is Halloween, by DOROTHY BROWN THOMPSON	144
This Is the Hay That No Man Planted, by ELIZABETH COATSWORTH	129
Threnody, by JOHN FARRAR	115
Trains at Night, by FRANCES FROST	7
Turtle Soup, by LEWIS CARROLL	169
Wash the Dishes, Wipe the Dishes, MOTHER GOOSE	169
West Wind's Secret, The, by MARY JANE CARR	89
What Could Be Lovelier Than to Hear, by ELIZABETH COATSWORTH	123
When a Ring's Around the Moon, by MARY JANE CARR	95
When Jacky's a Very Good Boy, MOTHER GOOSE	167
White Horses, by WINIFRED HOWARD	137
Who Has Seen the Wind?, by CHRISTINA G. ROSSETTI	108
Who Loves the Rain, by FRANCES SHAW	110
	185

Who Pilots Ships, *by* DANIEL WHITEHEAD HICKY	138
Who'll Buy My Valley Lilies?, *by* ELEANOR FARJEON	72
Who's In, *by* ELIZABETH FLEMING	166
Why Does It Snow?, *by* LAURA E. RICHARDS	116
Willow Cats, The, *by* MARGARET WIDDEMER	65
Wind, The, *by* BETTY MILLER	109
Wind Has Such a Rainy Sound, The, *by* CHRISTINA G. ROSSETTI	133
Winds A-Blowing, *by* MAY JUSTUS	108
Word About Woodpiles, A, *by* NANCY BYRD TURNER	161
Words from an Old Spanish Carol, *by* RUTH SAWYER	149

INDEX OF FIRST LINES

A Boot and a Shoe and a Slipper	24
A bundle is a funny thing	147
A caravan from China comes	100
A child should have a pocket	26
"A four-leaf clover!" cried the Worm	63
A gypsy, a gypsy	12
A kite, a sky, and a good firm breeze	119
A little clown puppet began to fret	32
A little mountain spring I found	85
A poor old woman	86
A pretty little boy and a pretty little girl	25
A road might lead to anywhere	3
A ship sails up to Bideford	132
Above the stable	150
All aboard for Bombay	8
Along a road	121
Any way the old world goes	124
Apple blossoms look like snow	65
Beautiful Soup, so rich and green	169
Behind Devaney's barn I saw	56
Bells in the country	51
Big trucks with apples	52
Bless the four corners of this house	166
Blessed of the Lord be his land	92
Blow, wind, blow! And go, mill, go	59
Boats sail on the rivers	102
Boats that carry sugar	135
Bob has blown a hundred eggs	55
Bobby Shaftoe's gone to sea	21
Bright stars, light stars	
Bryan O'Lin had no breeches to wear	21
But give me holly, bold and jolly	146
Come up in the orchard with grass to your knees	110
Cross patch	160
Daffy-down-dilly has come up to town	78
Dark Danny has eyes	83
Deedle, deedle, dumpling, my son John	172
Desolate and lone	134
Do you see that willow standing	89
Does the Elephant remember	84
From groves of spice	174
From the top of the bluff, where the wind blows free	8
Gay go up and gay go down	79
Girls and boys, come out to play	31

187

Glad that I live am I	66
Goblins on the doorstep	144
God bless the master of this house	152
Growing in the vale	62
Happened that the moon was up before I went to bed	96
Have you seen the lights of London how they twinkle, twinkle, twinkle	80
He said his legs were stiff and sore	59
High adventure	6
Hump, the Escalator, slid	77
I always wanted	165
I climbed up on the merry-go-round	34
I had a rich old great-aunt	54
I had a silver buckle	25
I know a little cupboard	168
I like the fall	113
I like the whistle of trains at night	7
I like to wear my party frock	17
I listened, there was not a sound to hear	98
I love old maps made long ago	47
I love our old pear tree	30
I saw a great barge	10
I saw a star slide down the sky	99
I wanted a rifle for Christmas	147
I'd asked the grocer	73
If I had just one penny	143
If once you have slept on an island	11

I'll tell you how the sun rose	103
I'm glad that I	78
In rain or shine; in heat or snow	71
In the other gardens	112
Indian pipe and moccasin flower	88
Islands and peninsulas, continents and capes	46
It is raining	78
It's fun to clean house	159
I've got a new book from my Grandfather Hyde	44
Jack Sprat's pig	57
Jennie, come tie my	21
Life isn't dreary	161
Little Tillie Turtle	5
Little white horses are out on the sea	139
May mornings are merry	43
Mexican Jo and Mexican Jane	58
Midsummer Eve, a year ago, my mother she commanded	90
Mistress Mary, quite contrary	171
Moonbeam steps down the silken ladder	97
Multiplication is vexation	46
My button gloves are very white	142
My dear Daddie bought a mansion	157
My father he left me three acres of land	53
My goodness, my goodness	148

My sweetheart's a Sailor	9	Roger Francis	45
My zipper suit is bunny-brown	20	Rumbling and rattly good green Bus	69
Near where I live there is a lake	64	Sea Shell, Sea Shell	127
		Shall I tell you who will come	149
New shoes, new shoes	23	Shop of dreams is up on a hill	173
Nine-o'clock Bell	43	Sing hey! Sing hey	146
No feathered bird can weave	104	Sleeping in a cabin is as jolly as can be	10
Nose, nose, jolly red nose	167	Slowly, silently, now the moon	98
O dandelion, rich and haughty	62	Some hae meat and canna eat	167
O Sailor, come ashore	128	Something told the wild geese	107
October gave a party	114	Sometimes a little house will please	155
Off the coast of Ireland	133	St. Patrick's day is with us	141
Oh, what do the sea shells murmur	127	Stars over snow	99
On a little green knoll	158	Staying in bed and being sick	44
On market days we always call	70	Susie's galoshes	24
		Swing, swing	36
On the dusty earth-drum	122	Thanksgiving Day I like to see	145
On tip-toe comes the gentle dark	174	The andirons were the dragons	160
One day when we went walking	29	The autumn wind's a pirate	111
Our history sings of centuries	46	The axe has cut the forest down	55
Our house is small	156	The big swing-tree is green again	35
Over crimson clover-seas	58	The cart that carries hay	57
Pipe thee high and pipe thee low	40	The city has streets	52
Polly put the kettle on	167	The city sleeps in its uncon-cern, but the highways are awake	75
Poor little Lucy	22		
Queen Anne, Queen Anne, has washed her lace	63	"The door is shut fast . . ."	166
			189

The drum's a very quiet fellow	38	The wind has such a rainy sound	133
The elevator car in the elevator shaft	76	The year's at the spring	92
		There was an old lady	163
The great Pacific railway	7	They call them pussy willows	65
The harvesters—they say themselves	60	This air that blows in from the sea	130
The hollyhock with crimson bells	171	This dawn when the mountain-cherry lifts	142
The lights from the parlour and kitchen shone out	101	This is the hay that no man planted	129
The little white mermaidens live in the sea	128	Through all the frozen winter	120
		"Thumbs in the thumb-place . . ."	19
The monkey and the organ man	48	Thump—Thud! Who is throwing	112
The Moon's the North Wind's cooky	97	Tic-Tic-Tic	118
The night is like an old cat	101	Tonight when the hoar frost falls on the wood	151
The North Wind is a beggar	108		
The other day I went upstairs	18		
The popcorn man	74	Up in the barn where they keep the hay	39
The red leaves fall upon the lake	115		
The room was low and small and kind	164	Walk fast in snow	118
		Wash the dishes, wipe the dishes	169
The roadway has a flinten face	4	We built a hut, my brother and I	37
The sea has a laugh	131		
The sea-wash never ends	131	We went to a circus in the town	170
The snow is soft, and how it squashes	119	What a gay	44
		What can I give Him	148
The spider weaves his silver wire	170	What could be lovelier than to hear	123
The storm snapped its fingers	136	What's the good of breathing	117
The way they scrub	20	When Bill gives me a book, I know	146
The wee folk will be tripping	95		
The white-housed village	56		

190

When frost is shining on the trees	162
When I go walking down the street	72
When I try to skate	33
When I'm a little older	35
When I'm in bed at night	172
When Jacky's a very good boy	167
When school is out, we love to follow	48
When the green woods laugh with the voice of joy	88
Where did the little boy go, you say	61
White sheep, white sheep	102
Who but the wind	109
Who comes dancing over the snow	141
Who has seen the wind	108
Who loves the rain	110
Who pilots ships knows all a heart can know	138
Who'll buy my valley lilies	72
"Why does it snow? Why does it snow?"	116
Winds through the olive trees	150
Would you tell me the way to Somewhere	13
You should hear	**85**